Steam Trapping and Air Venting

Steam Trapping and Air Venting

L. G. Northcroft
OBE, BSc. (Eng.), CEng., FIMech. E, FCIBS, Hon. FIPlant E.

W. M. Barber
MA (Cantab.), CEng., FIMech. E., FCIBS, Hon. FIPlant E

Hutchinson of London

Hutchinson & Co. (Publishers) Ltd
3 Fitzroy Square, London W1P 6JD

London Melbourne Sydney Auckland
Wellington Johannesburg and agencies
throughout the world

First published 1944
Reprinted 1945
Second edition 1946
Reprinted 1947, 1950
Third edition 1952
Reprinted 1955, 1958, 1961
Fourth edition 1968
Reprinted 1972, 1974
Fifth edition 1979

Set in VIP Times Roman by Preface Ltd, Salisbury, Wilts.

Printed in Great Britain by The Anchor Press Ltd
and bound by Wm Brendon & Son Ltd,
both of Tiptree, Essex

ISBN 0 09 138190 8

Contents

Introduction

Because of the change by industry to the metric system, there has been a growing demand for *Steam Trapping and Air Venting* to be made available with SI metric units of measurement in place of imperial ones.

Meeting this need has also provided the opportunity for revising some sections of the book.

Practice has changed following the availability of balanced pressure traps and air vents with stainless steel elements. By making them very much more resistant to adverse conditions, this development has revitalized these very important and useful steam traps. The demise of the very reliable, but large and expensive, open-top bucket trap has also caused some changes to be made.

Sadly, while the 5th edition was being prepared, Mr Northcroft died. This book, which he originally wrote himself, is a testimony to the many years he spent educating engineers and management in the efficient use of steam.

Our thanks are due to Mr John Marr, who has checked the numerous metric conversions and calculations, Mr Norman Lewis and his team for the new and revised illustrations, and Mrs Sheila Cripps for typing the revised text.

W. M. Barber

1 Steam and condensate

Steam traps are regarded by many engineers as a necessary evil. Let us agree at once that they can be a serious evil; but if their function and their application are fully understood, they should give no more trouble than any other item of steam plant, and their correct use can be a sure means of fuel economy or increased production.

This book is written in the belief that it will show that many of the evils connected with steam traps have been brought about not by steam traps themselves but because of incomplete knowledge of the way they should be used.

Steam raising

We must start at the very beginning and ask why we generate steam at all. Steam is not an end in itself. It is, within the scope of this book, produced solely to serve as a convenient carrier of energy in the form of heat and pressure.

The SI metric unit of heat is the joule (J), and it takes 4.19 joules to raise the temperature of 1 gram of water through 1 °C.

The chemical energy which is contained in a boiler fuel is converted into heat energy when the fuel is burned. This heat energy is transmitted through the wall of the boiler furnace to the water. The temperature of the water is raised by this addition of heat until the water boils.

Heat energy which produces a rise of temperature when it is passed into the water is known as the Specific enthalpy of water and is given the symbol h_f. Many engineers will know it as Sensible heat. The first effect of burning fuel in a boiler furnace is, therefore, to add Specific enthalpy to the water. It is practice to reckon that the Specific enthalpy of water is nil at 0 °C; so to raise the temperature of 1 kg of water from 0 °C to 100 °C (atmospheric boiling point) requires 419 kJ. If the water put into the boiler is at a temperature above 0 °C it will obviously need less heat to raise the water to boiling point and less fuel will be needed to supply this Specific enthalpy.

As more heat passes from the furnace to the water, the temperature of the water does not rise so long as the water is at atmospheric pressure, but the heat is used in vaporizing the water and converting it into steam.

Heat energy which produces a change of state without a change in temperature is known as Specific enthalpy of evaporation (again many will know it as Latent heat) and has the symbol h_{f_g}. As heat continues to pass from the furnace to the water, more and more water is changed to steam. If this steam has no outlet from the boiler, a pressure is set up by the steam on the surface of the water. The effect of this pressure is to raise the temperature at which the water boils. This calls for a further supply of Specific enthalpy of water to keep it at its new higher temperature; but as the pressure and temperature rise so the amount of Specific enthalpy of evaporation needed to convert the higher temperature water into steam is reduced.

The rise in the Specific enthalpy of the water is greater than the fall in the Specific enthalpy of evaporation so the Specific enthalpy of the steam increases, but only slightly as the pressure increases.

The Specific enthalpy of dry 'saturated' steam at any pressure (previously called Total heat) is the sum of the Specific enthalpies of water and evaporation and has the symbol h_g. ('Saturated' steam is steam generated in contact with water.) So we can say that

$$h_f + h_{f_g} = h_g.$$

The heat content and other properties of steam are set out in the Steam tables which will be found at the end of this book.

A simple picture of process steam generation will be found in Figure 1. The graph shows the number of kJ present in each kg of steam as Specific enthalpy of steam, Specific enthalpy of evaporation and Specific enthalpy of water at various steam pressures and as Specific enthalpy of water at atmospheric pressure. It shows the variation of the heat content as the steam pressure and temperature vary.

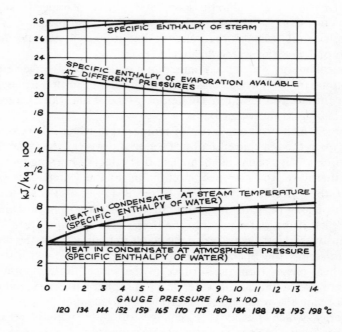

Figure 1

Steam pressure is described as so many kilopascals (kPa) and may be given either as 'Gauge pressure' or 'Absolute pressure'. (Another unit of pressure in common use is the 'bar'. 1 bar is equal to 100 kPa.)

Gauge pressure is that shown on an ordinary pressure gauge and is the pressure above that of the atmosphere.

Absolute pressure is the pressure above a theoretical pressureless state which would exist if there were no weight of atmosphere to cause pressure. Zero on the Absolute pressure scale is therefore the pressure of a perfect vacuum.

The weight of the atmosphere varies according to height and to weather conditions, but the average weight at sea level is 101.3 kPa. Zero on the Gauge pressure scale is therefore 101.3 kPa on the Absolute pressure scale.

The weight of the atmosphere is also conveniently measured by the height of a column of mercury which it will hold up in a closed evacuated tube. This average height is approximately 760 mm. So 101.3 kPa equals 760 mm of mercury (Hg).

Pressures below zero gauge are often measured as so many millimetres of mercury.

Coming back to our boiler, if the steam is taken away faster than it is being generated, the surface of the water will be below atmospheric pressure. The effect of this will be to lower the boiling point, lower the Specific enthalpy of the water and increase the Specific enthalpy of evaporation. At 385 mm Hg vacuum, which is equivalent to an absolute pressure of 50 kPa, the temperature of the water and steam is 81 °C (see Table H, page 218), the Specific enthalpy of water per kilogram is 340 kJ, the Specific enthalpy of evaporation is 2305 kJ and the Specific enthalpy of steam is 2645 kJ.

At atmospheric pressure, the temperature is 100 °C, the Specific enthalpy of water per kg is 419 kJ, the Specific enthalpy of evaporation is 2257 kJ and the Specific enthalpy of steam is 2676 kJ.

At 1400 kPa gauge pressure, the temperature has risen to 198 °C, the Specific enthalpy of water per kg has risen to 845 kJ, the Specific enthalpy of evaporation has fallen to 1947 kJ and the Specific enthalpy of steam has risen slighly to 2792 kJ.

These points are being made to illustrate two important facts:

That it requires only 116 more heat units to generate 1 kg of steam at 1400 kPa pressure than that required at atmospheric pressure – only $4\frac{1}{2}$ %.

That at 1400 kPa pressure no less than 30 % of the heat in the steam is Specific enthalpy of water; while at atmospheric pressure the proportion is only 16 %.

Wet steam

So far we have considered only the heat content of dry saturated steam. But steam is seldom dry and not always saturated.

When steam is generated in a boiler, the water surface is turbulent and droplets of water are thrown up into the steam. Particularly when steam is being extracted from the boiler at a high rate, the movement of the steam towards the outlet will carry these droplets away and into the steam system.

Steam which contains these particles of water in a finely divided state is called wet steam. If 1 kg of wet steam is made up of, say, 95 % dry steam and 5 % water particles, it is said to have a dryness fraction of .95.

The Specific enthalpy of 1 kg of wet steam is less than that of dry steam because the water particles have escaped without receiving any Specific enthalpy of evaporation. The Specific enthalpy of wet steam is made up of h_f, the Specific enthalpy of water and $q \times h_{f_g}$, q being the dryness fraction and h_{f_g} the Specific enthalpy of evaporation.

For example the Specific enthalpy of steam of 1 kg at 1400 kPa gauge pressure having a dryness fraction (q) of 0.94 is

$$h_g = h_f + q\, h_{f_g}$$

$$= 845 + 0.94 \times 1947$$
$$= 845 + 1830$$
$$= 2675 \text{ kJ}$$

This is 117 kJ less per kg than the Specific enthalpy of steam of dry steam.

The important effect of a small percentage of wetness in the steam leaving the boiler will be realized when we consider that steam at 1400 kPa gauge, if it contains 6 % of water particles, has less Specific enthalpy of steam than dry steam at atmospheric pressure.

Superheat

In the era, now generally passed, of the Lancashire type of boiler having a large steam space above the water, it was often possible to provide a dryer within the space before the steam left the boiler. This took the form of a series of baffles so designed that water particles were deposited and left behind. From the Economic type of boiler onwards to the modern Packaged boiler this was no longer practical; furthermore the problem of ensuring that only dry steam was delivered was greatly increased by the tendency of such boilers, given incorrect water treatment and the incidence of peak loads, to 'prime' and for boiler water to be carried over into the steam main.

Under such conditions it is very necessary to fit a steam dryer, often but less accurately called a steam separator, in the steam main immediately after the boiler. (The matter is discussed further on page 24.)

The second method is to take the wet steam away from the water to another source of heat. The source of heat is the waste heat in the flue gases from the boiler, and the separate vessel is the superheater. The extra heat first gives the missing Specific enthalpy of evaporation to any water particles and turns the wet steam into dry saturated steam. When there is no longer any water present, the steam itself absorbs the extra heat and becomes superheated steam.

Superheated steam at a given pressure can be at any temperature above that of saturated steam. It, in general, behaves like a gas and not like a vapour. For example, it expands when heated and contracts when cooled. Saturated steam, by contrast, condenses when cooled.

It follows that superheating increases the Specific enthalpy of steam, but not by a very great amount.

For example, the Specific enthalpy of steam of 1 kg of steam at 1400 kPa which has been superheated by 50 °C is 2917 kJ. Although the temperature of the steam has been raised from 198 °C to 248 °C the Specific enthalpy has been raised only from 2792 to 2917 kJ.

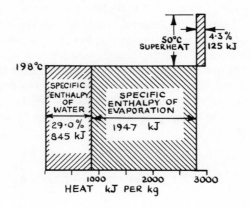

Figure 2

Figure 2 shows, to scale, the relative values of the Specific enthalpies of water and evaporation and the superheat in 1 kg of steam at 1400 kPa and 50 °C superheat.

The Specific enthalpy of water provides 29 %.

The Specific enthalpy of evaporation provides 66.7 %.

The superheat provides 4.3 %.

The reason why only 125 kJ were added to 1 kg of steam on heating it 50 °C at 1400 kPa gauge is because the average Specific Heat Capacity of superheated steam at this pressure and temperature is 2.5 kJ/kg.

The Specific Heat Capacity of any substance is the quantity of heat required to raise the temperature of 1 kg by 1 °C. The Specific Heat Capacity of superheated steam varies according to pressure and temperature. The higher the pressure, the higher the Specific Heat Capacity; the higher the temperature the lower the Specific Heat Capacity.

It will be seen that superheating provides a valuable safeguard against loss of heat-content due to wet steam conditions, particularly when the steam is to be used for generating power. But the superheating of steam brings about another set of problems when the steam is required for its heat value alone, for process or heating plant.

Steam volume

Dry saturated steam at atmospheric pressure takes up a lot of room. 1 kg of it fills 1.67 m³.

As steam pressures rise, so steam becomes more compact. At 110 kPa gauge 1 kg occupies only 0.84 m³. At 340 kPa gauge the volume has halved again to 0.42 m³.

By the time the pressure has risen to 1400 kPa the volume of 1 kg has shrunk to 0.13 m³.

This is a valuable point. We remember that steam at this pressure has only $4\frac{1}{2}$ % more heat per kilogram than atmospheric steam, but we can get more than eight times the amount of steam at the higher pressure into the same space.

If the steam should not be dry and we decide to superheat it, we find that the volume factor now starts to work against us, because steam expands when it is superheated. The behaviour of superheated steam is sufficiently like that of a perfect gas for an approximate formula to be available to find the volume of superheated steam under any conditions of constant pressure.

If V_s is the volume of 1 kg of saturated steam, V the volume of 1 kg of superheated steam at the same pressure, both measured in m³, and t °C the amount of superheat

$$V = V_s (1 + 0.0033t)$$

For example, the volume of 1 kg of steam at 1400 kPa gauge, superheated by 50 °C, is

$$V = 0.13 (1 + 0.0033 \times 50)$$
$$= 0.15 \text{ m}^3$$

The heat content of 1 kg of steam at 1400 kPa was increased from 2792 to 2917 kJ or 5 % by superheating. But the volume was increased from 0.13 to 0.15 m³ or 15.4 %. Therefore, the heat content per cubic metre of steam has been decreased as a result of superheating.

A process steam circuit

In this book we are thinking of steam which has been generated to be a source of heat or a source of power. Let us consider the use of steam as a conveyor of heat to process plant.

When the boiler stop valve is opened, steam flows at once along the pipe which is to take it to the process plant and it leaves its source of heat. The steam may be wet, dry or superheated, but let us assume that it is dry and saturated. The carrying pipe is cold and is surrounded by cold air. Heat is extracted from the steam so that drops of water form on the cold surfaces, having given up their Specific enthalpy of evaporation to the pipe.

The steam flows on into the steam space of the process plant. More Specific enthalpy of evaporation passes from the steam to all the cold surrounding surfaces. Some is wasted by radiation and convection from the outside surfaces of the plant; some does useful work by passing through the wall of the steam space to the material which has to be heated.

Heat transmission

The rate at which heat energy in the form of either Specific enthalpy of water or Specific enthalpy of evaporation flows from the steam to the surrounding metal surfaces depends on a number of factors, one of the most important being the difference in temperature between the two. Because the whole story of the transmission of heat from steam through a heating surface is so vital to efficient plant operation it is dealt with in some detail in Chapter 4. For the moment we will consider the temperature difference between the steam and its surroundings which may conveniently be called the 'temperature head'. When this is high, heat will flow rapidly; when it is low heat will flow slowly.

When steam is first admitted to the process plant, the temperature head is high, because the metal of the steam space is cold and the material to be heated is cold. Metals are good conductors of heat and the temperature of the walls tends to rise quickly, thus reducing the temperature head. The outside walls of the steam space are heated above the temperature of the surrounding air and so begin to lose heat by radiation and convection, but only slowly. The inside walls of the steam space begin to transmit heat to the process material as soon as their temperature is raised by the steam.

This transmission of heat is generally much greater because the process material is a better absorber of heat. Because the process material is confined and, unlike the outside air, cannot easily dissipate the heat which it is receiving, its temperature is raised. This decreases the temperature head and reduces the heat flow from the steam.

Condensation

The heat provided by dry saturated steam is, so far as we have seen, Specific enthalpy of evaporation. This is all transmitted at the temperature of saturated steam corresponding to the steam pressure. Since it is only the Specific enthalpy of evaporation in steam which has changed it from water, as soon as this is removed it changes back – it condenses. The amount of Specific enthalpy of evaporation which is given up by 1 kg of steam in condensing is the same as the amount which was put into it in vaporizing.

The condensate which is formed is at the temperature of the saturated steam and it still contains all its Specific enthalpy of water. There is still a temperature head between the condensate and its surroundings, so it gives up heat to them. But the loss of Specific enthalpy of water, unlike the loss of Specific enthalpy of evaporation, produces a drop in temperature. The condensate cools and in doing so reduces the temperature head between it and the process material. If the condensate were allowed to stay in the steam space it would go on giving up Specific enthalpy of water until all the temperature head had been used up and the heating of the process material would stop. Specific enthalpy of water in process plant is therefore only of value so long as the temperature head is sufficient to allow the passage of heat to the process material at a rate which the process demands.

Superheat in process plant

If the superheating of steam is a valuable means of drying it and ensures the full amount of Specific enthalpy of evaporation being present, it would seem that superheat might help in preventing the formation of condensate in process plant.

Let us consider a typical example. We can feed our process plant either with dry saturated steam at 350 kPa gauge or with superheated steam at the same pressure and 50 °C superheat.

1 kg of dry saturated steam has 2120 kJ of Specific enthalpy of evaporation and 2744 kJ of Specific enthalpy of steam and occupies 0.41 m^3.

1 kg of superheated steam has 2120 kJ of Specific enthalpy of evaporation, 111 kJ of superheat, 2855 kJ of Specific enthalpy of steam and occupies 0.46 m^3.

The steam space of the process plant is a certain fixed amount – suppose it to be 0.05 m^3. Dry saturated steam in this space will contain $2120 \times \dfrac{0.05}{0.41}$ or 259 kJ of heat which can be used before condensation. Superheated steam will contain $2231 \times \dfrac{0.05}{0.46}$ or 243 kJ. Thus the heat readily available in the steam space is greater if saturated steam is used.

Against this, the temperature head, using superheated steam, will be greater by 50 °C, and so heat should flow more quickly to the process material. As soon as any superheat units are taken away, however, the temperature drops. Moreover there are only 111 kJ available in each kilogram before the temperature is down to saturation temperature. If the process is such that its heat requirements can be met by the small amount available as superheat (and there are such processes) then the greater temperature head available with superheat will be an advantage. If the heat requirements cannot be met by the superheat alone, the presence of superheated steam in the steam space will be found to be a definite disadvantage to production.

Superheated steam behaves like a perfect gas and not like a saturated vapour. The flow of heat from the superheated steam core of the steam space to the surface of heat transfer must be by conduction only while any superheat remains. Saturated steam on the other hand gives up its heat to the surface by moving to it as steam condenses.

Furthermore, if part of a surface is being heated by the superheat in the steam and part by saturated steam, there may be an undesirable difference in temperature between one part of the face and another.

Nevertheless there are advantages in superheating at the boiler as will be made clear when considering steam transmission.

Condensate removal

So, as superheating does not help in the plant itself, we are still left with the problem of getting rid of the condensate from the steam space after no more use can be made of its Specific enthalpy of water.

The steam has now done the work for which it was generated, but both money and fuel have been used to provide these heat units which cannot be used in the process itself. The efficiency of the whole process cycle depends in large measure on what is done with this heat in the condensate.

One thing is certain, the condensate must be removed from the steam space. Suppose we allow the condensate to drain away from the bottom of the steam space through a pipe to atmosphere. The condensate gets away quickly enough, because one end of the pipe is at steam pressure and the other end at atmospheric pressure. But when the condensate has all been pushed out, the steam follows it.

This will not do, because we are now wasting valuable Specific enthalpy of evaporation as well as Specific enthalpy of water, so we put a valve on the condensate outlet pipe and close it down to throttle the steam loss. We set the valve opening so that there is just enough room to pass a steady stream of condensate. Then we find that at times condensate is holding up in the steam space and at other times steam is blowing.

Variable condensate formation

When the temperature head between the steam and the process material is high, heat is passing quickly from the steam, and condensation is rapid but when the temperature head is low, condensation is slow. A fixed valve opening cannot possibly cater for both these conditions.

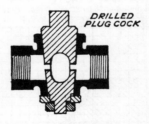

DRILLED
PLUG COCK

Figure 3

It was once a practice to use a drilled plug cock on the drain outlet, as shown in Figure 3. The operator turns the plug round when the process is started up so that the condensate is discharged through a large opening. When the process has advanced and the condensate rate has fallen, the plug cock is turned so that condensate is discharged through the small opening.

This method assumes that condensate is being made at only two rates.

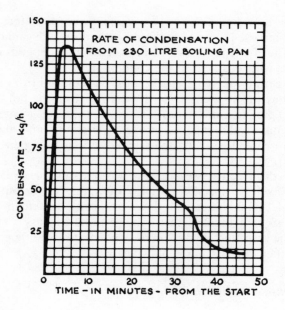

Figure 4

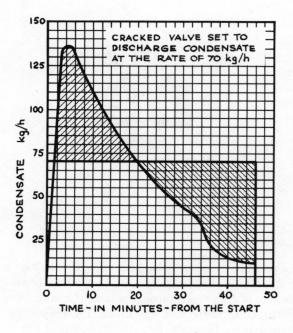

Figure 5

Figure 4 gives a typical picture of how condensation really does take place in a process unit.

The example shows the variation of condensate rate in heating up the contents of a 230 litre boiling pan.

The maximum rate of condensate is 136 kg per hour, the minimum rate is 13 kg per hour.

Figure 5 shows what would happen to this process if the condensate were drained through a cracked valve set to discharge condensate at the rate of 70 kg per hour. For the first $1\frac{1}{2}$ minutes the valve would blow steam. For the next $18\frac{1}{2}$ minutes the valve would hold up water in the steam space and slow down the process – about 9.5 kg of water would be held back in this time. This excess water would be discharged when the condensate rate had dropped below 70 kg per hour. It would take about 22 minutes for this to pass. Then steam would blow, nearly full bore, for the last 4 minutes.

This method has not only wasted much valuable steam, but has also held up production.

Figure 6 shows what would happen if the condensate were drained through a drilled plug cock.

The full passage through the plug is designed to pass 100 kg per hour and is open for 22 minutes; the drilled passage is designed to pass 35 kg per hour and is open for the last 24 minutes.

Steam blows, for the first 2 minutes, even more violently than through the cracked valve, because the opening is larger. Condensate is held up in the steam

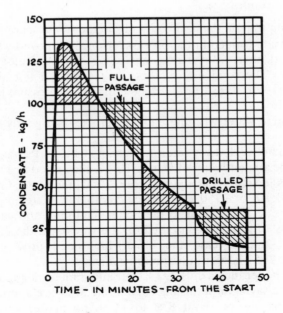

Figure 6

space for the next 10 minutes – 4 kg is held up this time – slowing up the process, but not so seriously as before. In the next 10 minutes, before the plug cock is turned to bring the small hole into action, 3 kg of the excess water is discharged. The condensate rate is once more greater than can be discharged through the small opening, and there is already 1 kg of water left in the steam space. Once more the process is slowed up and goes on for the next 12 minutes during which another 3 kg of water has been added to the 1 already held up. This excess water is discharged during the next 10 minutes, and the process speeds up again. For the last two minutes steam is blowing through the drilled plug cock, but not so badly as it was through the cracked valve.

This method of removing condensate – which was not at all uncommon – has also wasted steam and slowed down production.

The examples chosen have shown the inefficiency of both cracked valves and plug cocks, even when the system is operated in the best possible manner. In practice cracked valves are not scientifically cracked, nor were plug cocks turned at the theoretically correct moment. No process steam cycle can hope for efficiency if such methods of removing condensate are employed.

If there were installed on the drain outlet from the steam space, a valve which would automatically open to allow condensate to pass at the rate at which it was forming, and which would automatically shut so that steam could not blow, there would be no steam loss and no hold up of production. Such an automatic valve is a steam trap.

The use of clean condensate

By fitting a steam trap on the drain outlet from the steam space we have ensured that the condensate formed in the process has been removed when it can do no more useful work there. But it does not follow that it cannot do useful work somewhere else. The condensate is hot, having most if not all of its Specific enthalpy of water left; it is soft water; and it may have pressure behind it to push it somewhere else.

One place where water with these characteristics is urgently wanted is at the boiler.

You may remember that dry saturated steam at 1400 kPa has 30 % of its heat locked up as Specific enthalpy of water. This is illustrated in Figure 7.

If the boiler is fed with cold water at, say, 10 °C, the boiler fuel must provide 2792 – (4.186 × 10) or 2750 kJ of Specific enthalpy of steam per kilogram.

If the condensate is returned to the boiler feed tank and care is taken that Specific enthalpy of water is conserved on the way back, the feed temperature may be 80 °C. In this case the boiler fuel need provide only 2792 – (4.186 × 80) or 2457 kJ per kilogram of steam.

The saving in boiler fuel is thus 293 kJ per kilogram of steam or 10.7 %. It will be found that the saving in returning condensate at above approximately 65 °C for boiler feed is always about 8 % to 11 %, no matter what the pressure conditions. If the condensate is wasted, it means that 10 tonnes of fuel will be

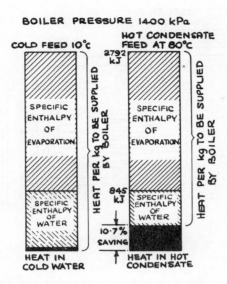

Figure 7

wasted per week on a plant using 100 tonnes, 1 tonne a week on a plant using 10 tonnes, and so on.

In addition to this saving of fuel, condensate is soft and can be used as boiler feed without treatment. This means an additional saving by cutting out feed water preparation.

Although hot condensate does make ideal boiler feed it may be thought that it is not convenient to take it back to the boiler house, because of the economics of distance, or because the amount available from one particular point is small, or because it is thought that the boiler feed water is already as hot as can be handled. Chapter 5 on 'Low potential heat' gives other suggestions for the heat usage in condensate. Only as a very last resort should this valuable boiler by-product be used for washing water or consigned to the drains.

The use of contaminated condensate

Unfortunately condensate discharged from process plant is not always clean. It may be that the process has brought the steam into direct contact with materials which are corrosive. Such condensate cannot be returned for boiler feed, although it holds valuable Specific enthalpy of water.

The first and most obvious way to get this heat back is by passing the contaminated condensate through a heat exchanger and allowing it to give up its heat either to a locally required liquid that needs heating, thus saving some live steam, or to raw boiler feed make-up water.

If the corrosive nature is such that very special and expensive materials would be required in the heat exchanger the method shown in Figure 8 could be

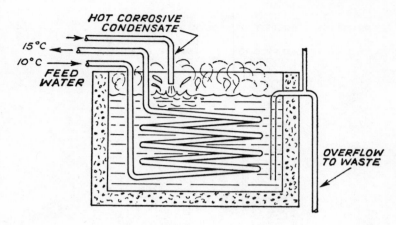

Figure 8

adopted using an easily replaceable coil in a concrete tank. In this example, from a rubber works, all the boiler feed water was heated 5 °C by the heat from the condensate from a battery of open vulcanizers.

Steam distribution

It will help to get a realistic outlook on a process steam distribution system if we start by considering the boiler as a store for raw material. It is a store for energy in the form of steam heat, which is itself a raw material for the process operation, just as clearly as is wool or sugar or a chemical component. The steam distribution system is thus shown to be the means by which this raw material is conveyed from the store to the process plant. But whereas you can see and stop material falling off a belt conveyor you can't so easily see heat material falling off a heat conveyor – except through the grosser errors such as leaking flanges and valves.

Nevertheless heat *is* dropping off its conveyor constantly through the insulation, however good or bad this may be, because in the last analysis it is inevitable that some losses should occur. Sometimes these losses are unnecessarily high, for example, as the result of the conveyor passing round three sides of a building for purely historical reasons.

The process plant to which the heat is being led has almost certainly been designed to work on dry saturated steam. But even if steam has been generated genuinely dry at the boiler – in itself something of a pious hope – it cannot possibly also be dry at the plant. On the contrary, as soon as the steam leaves the boiler on its way to the process plant, it gives up some of its Specific enthalpy of evaporation and begins to condense.

Condensation in the steam main will form initially on the wall of the pipe as a film of water. This will be dragged along by the steam velocity of perhaps 40 metres a second and at the same time gravity will act to make it thicker on the bottom of the main than on the sides. As soon as there is any disturbance to flow such as would be caused by a bend or valve, the water film will be picked up by the steam in the form of drops so adding to any water droplets already carried over from the boiler.

If the main is drained by appropriate steam trapping, as is described in a later chapter, the water on the bottom may be removed but not the high speed drops – and even the water film is being dragged along very rapidly and so needs a proper drain arresting point before it will flow down to the steam trap.

If the droplets of condensation from the main are allowed to pass through into the process unit they will interfere with the passage of Specific enthalpy of evaporation from the dry steam to the metal. In themselves the drops have no Specific enthalpy of evaporation, so contribute nothing to the process. In draining down the metal surface they add to the thickness of the water film that has legitimately formed as a result of the passage of heat from the dry steam to the metal. This thicker film increases the resistance to heat flow and lowers the temperature of the metal wall, thus slowing production in the plant.

The better the quality of the steam, that is, the less water it contains at the plant the higher will be the possible rate of production. There are three ways of improving steam quality.

If the boiler plant allows, it is worth considering slighly superheating the steam before it leaves for the process plant – not to provide superheat at the plant, but to allow the unneeded superheat to be dissipated in pipe losses rather than the needed Specific enthalpy of evaporation. This course cannot mean that all process units are fed with dry saturated steam, because they will be at different distances from the boiler and have different heat losses in their feed mains; but if the choice is made based on the largest steam user, much good will have been achieved.

A second, straightforward and simple, method of obtaining dry steam at the plant is by the use of steam separators. Their use is better exemplified by their alternative name, steam dryers, by which they will be known in the following section only.

Steam dryers

A steam dryer separates water particles from flowing steam by two distinct methods, both of which operate by the difference in density of steam and water.

Figure 9 shows an impact dryer. This design has a double purpose. Steam flows through an increasing area, its velocity falls and some water drops out of suspension. The steam direction changes and the heavier water drops impinge on a shaped surface down which they run out of contact with the continuing steam flow.

Figure 10 is a different conception. In this dryer the steam velocity is first maintained but the flow is given a twist so that the heavier water droplets are flung out of suspension by centrifugal force against the sides of the vessel, then the flow area is increased so that the steam velocity drops to minimize pick-up of separated water.

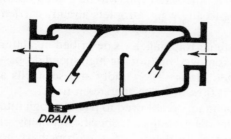

Figure 9   Figure 10

   Reference has already been made (page 12) to the use of a dryer in the steam main immediately after a boiler. This is not so much to take care of condensation due to heat loss in the distribution system as to prevent boiler water actually being carried over into the main. This can cause great trouble with corrosion in mains and gumming-up of instruments and automatic valves, besides producing the normal hazards of wet steam.

   Steam dryers, when used for preventing bad effects of wet steam in process units, should be fitted as near as possible to the units themselves. A small dryer, drained by an appropriate steam trap, in such a position will give the best steam quality that plant conditions permit. If the ultimate output is required from steam heated plant this is certainly one of the additions that should be carried out.

Reducing steam pressures

There remains yet another way in which, perhaps incidentally for our purpose, steam quality becomes improved.

   The higher the pressure at which steam is generated the less space one kilogram of it takes up and the more steam can be pushed along a pipe line. Or, if a certain amount of steam has to be transmitted, the smaller the pipe which is needed to carry it.

   By reducing to a minimum the size of pipe required to carry the steam we have done two things – we have reduced the capital cost of the transmission plant and we have reduced the heat losses from it.

   But one kilogram of steam at high pressure is not so valuable for process work as one kilogram at a lower pressure; because the higher the pressure, the lower the Specific enthalpy of evaporation per kilogram.

   Process plant is generally designed to give a certain output at a certain steam pressure and temperature. There must be some temperature head between the steam and the process material. This will determine the low limit of steam pressure. The higher the steam pressure above this low limit the greater the temperature head will be and, within limits, the greater the rate of production.

But the higher the steam pressure the less the Specific enthalpy of evaporation which is available per kilogram and so the more kilograms of steam required to give the same heating effect.

The steam pressure for any given process job is therefore a nice choice between output and fuel consumption. The steam pressure for best generation and transmission is quite another matter. Within the permissible limits of the plant, the higher the pressure the better.

As a result of these quite separate conditions it may be found that it is correct to generate at a higher pressure than the pressure at which the steam is to be used.

Let us assume that we are generating dry saturated steam at 1400 kPa gauge and we want to use dry saturated steam at 350 kPa.

The steam gives up Specific enthalpy of evaporation to the steam main and by the time that it reaches the first process take-off, each kilogram has lost, say, 40 kJ in making up pipe losses (dryness fraction 0.98).

The Specific enthalpy of 1400 kPa steam which was 2792 kJ per kg has been reduced to 2752 kJ.

The steam now passes through a pressure reducing valve to 350 kPa on the first process branch.

The Specific enthalpy of 350 kPa steam is 2744 kJ per kg. Assuming that no heat loss occurs in the reducing valve (in practice there must be some), the wet steam which went in at 1400 kPa has come out at 350 kPa not only dry but with 8 kJ per kg as superheat and so approximately 4 °C above saturation temperature.

By the time the main steam reaches the furthest process branch it may have lost another, say, 38 kJ per kg (dryness fraction now 0.96). The Specific enthalpy of the steam is reduced to 2714 kJ per kg. Here it passes through another pressure reducing valve and comes out at 350 kPa. Dry saturated steam at 350 kPa should have a Specific enthalpy of 2744 kJ per kg made up of 624 kJ enthalpy of water and 2120 kJ enthalpy of evaporation. Our process steam is short of this by 30 kJ of Specific enthalpy of evaporation or 1.1 % which is still water. But the dryness fraction has been improved from 0.96 to approximately 0.99.

It would be crazy to fit a reducing valve just in order to dry steam. However if such a valve must be used because of the pressure conditions of generation and usage, it is as well to consider where and why it should be fitted. If all the process plant is to be operated at a lower pressure than the boiler and the higher pressure boiler has been chosen merely to save capital on the distribution system, then obviously the pressure reduction should be made near to the plant. A moment's consideration should however be given to the possibility of reducing the pressure through an engine or an evaporator. You get much more for your high pressure that way than by degrading it through a reducing valve. This large question is dealt with at length in that wonderful book *The Efficient Use of Steam* by Sir Oliver Lyle.

If however low pressure steam is used only for certain of the process units, or if the pressures are different or need to be varied, it is probable that separate pressure reductions will be necessary. Lyle says, '. . . a reducing valve is, from a thermodynamic point of view, an invention of the devil . . .'. It is also true to say that it can be a devilish piece of equipment from every point of view if it is not properly chosen and installed – indeed like a steam trap.

There are three types of pressure reducing valves: those that employ an external source of power to operate the main valve through a pilot or relay valve; those that employ the steam pressure itself to operate the main valve through a pilot valve; and simpler, direct acting valves that are spring or weight-balanced. The first type are somewhat uncommon in the more normal process industries; they find their place on high pressure and high capacity installations and where extreme accuracy of process control pressures is needed.

Figure 11 shows a typical pilot operated valve of the second type. The main valve is normally operated by a diaphragm as shown or by a piston in the valve body.

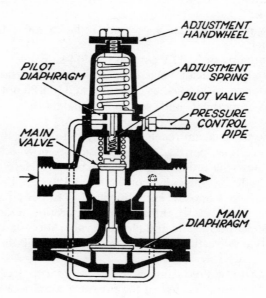

Figure 11

A direct acting reducing valve is cheaper, but control is not and cannot be as accurate as with the pilot operated type; nor should the direct acting valve be expected to shut off steam completely at times of no demand without a noticeable rise in downstream pressure.

The correct sizing and installation of pressure reducing valves and their protection against water, scale and dirt build-up is vital if they are to give accurate and trouble-free service.

A power steam circuit

We have considered the use of steam as a conveyor of heat to process plant, let us now see if any additional problems arise when the steam is to be used as a source of power in engines.

As soon as the boiler stop valve is opened the steam will begin to lose heat to the pipe line along which it is flowing to the engine. If the steam is initially superheated it will drop in temperature; if it is initially dry saturated it will become wet.

When the inlet valve to the engine is opened, steam flows into the steam space of the engine, of whatever type it may be, and expands. Heat is extracted from the steam by the walls of the steam space and is a total loss to the engine. There is a heat drop, or a fall in the Specific enthalpy of the steam during the act of expansion.

The amount of heat drop during expansion is found from an examination of the entropy of the steam before and after. This does not seem to be the place to enter into a description of a steam property which has no direct bearing on our main argument. Suffice it to say that as a result of expansion, the steam does work in the engine. Steam which is superheated on entry loses some or all of its superheat during expansion and may leave the steam space either still superheated or dry or wet. Steam which is dry saturated on entry will lose some of its Specific enthalpy of evaporation and will leave wet.

The presence of condensate in an engine steam space before expansion will, at the best, take up space which should be occupied by steam and will, at the worst, cause damage to the engine itself. It is of the utmost importance that condensate should not be allowed to flow into the engine from the steam main, but that it should be drained away through a steam trap.

If the steam is dry and saturated at the boiler, it is essential for the most efficient working of the engine that a separator should be fitted at the inlet.

Superheat in power plant

If the steam can possibly be superheated at the boiler and if the engine is designed for superheat working, then superheat should most certainly be used in power plant – this is one major difference between process and power circuits.

Whatever the type of power unit, superheat will help to reduce condensation when starting from cold. Superheat will also increase the power output by delaying condensation during the expansion stage. In turbines dryer steam at the exhaust end will decrease the erosion of blades.

Although reciprocating steam engines are seldom found in industry today, the table, which gives the typical steam consumption of various types of engine using dry saturated steam and steam superheated by 50 °C and 100 °C is interesting in highlighting the very apparent advantages of superheating.

Exhaust steam

Although the steam after expansion in the engine has done the work for which it was generated, it still contains nearly all the heat units which were put into it.

Once again, as in the process cycle, the efficiency of the power steam cycle depends on what is done with this exhaust.

There are three main alternatives. The steam can be exhausted to atmosphere. If this is done, the remaining Specific enthalpy of evaporation is lost – and it may be from 80 % to 100 % of the whole Specific enthalpy of evaporation, depending on the exhaust steam quality; all the Specific enthalpy of water is lost and all the soft condensate is lost.

The steam can be exhausted to a condenser. This will improve the efficiency of the power plant. The Specific enthalpy of evaporation in the exhaust steam will still be lost and the Specific enthalpy of evaporation of low pressure steam is a very large percentage of its Specific enthalpy of steam. Some of the Specific enthalpy of water in the condensate will be saved if the condensate is returned for boiler feed.

	steam consumption – kg/MJ		
type of engine	*saturated steam*	*50 °C superheat*	*100 °C superheat*
simple non-condensing	35–55	24–46	22–43
compound non-condensing	23–34	18–30	16–27
compound condensing	16–27	12–24	11–21
simple Duplex steam pumps	146–244	98–195	–
turbines non-condensing	34–73	29–66	26–60
turbines condensing	15–50	12–46	11–42

The steam can be exhausted at any pressure and used as low pressure steam for process or heating work. The efficiency of the power plant itself will not be so great as it would be if a condenser were used. All the Specific enthalpy of evaporation can be put to good use. The Specific enthalpy of water in the condensate can be saved if the condensate is returned from the process or heating plant for boiler feed.

This third alternative is so very much more efficient than either of the others that it should always be adopted if possible. In considering the balance of power, process and heating loads which largely determines whether it can be used, it should not be forgotten that a neighbouring estalishment might be glad of low pressure steam if there is no use for it at the place where it is produced.

Desuperheaters

A mixed power and process circuit, such as indicated, gives rise to one special problem. For the purposes of power generation the steam should be superheated, for process use it should not. Power generation calls for pressures as high as the plant will permit, process use calls for pressures as low as the plant will permit. If the main process steam is taken from the superheated supply at the boiler and then has to be reduced, the superheat will be increased and the steam made even more unsuitable for process use. The main process supply may, of course, be taken from the saturated steam space in the boiler, and delivered dry by the use of reducing valves. This presents no special problem. The main process steam – or some of it – may be taken from the engine exhaust. This will be either wet, exactly dry (most unlikely) or still superheated. If it is wet, the use of separators is called for. If it is superheated, the amount of superheat may be so small that it is lost by the time the process plant is reached. This is ideal. But there may be so much superheat left that the steam is not in its best form for process use.

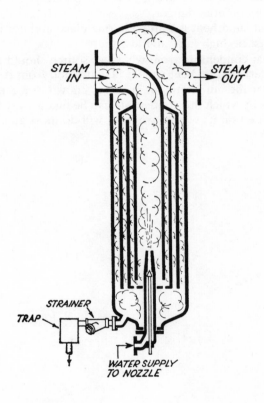

Figure 12

Figure 12 shows a section of a desuperheater. Superheated steam is fed downwards into the vessel and up into the main chamber. High pressure jets of atomized water are then sprayed into the steam. The amount of water is controlled by a thermostatic valve on the water supply which ensures that only so much water is admitted to maintain the temperature of the outgoing steam at a very few degrees above saturation temperature. The control can be set so as to ensure dry saturated steam at the first process using point.

Desuperheaters are also made of the 'surface type' instead of the 'spray type' described. These are in essence another form of evaporator and the operation is discussed in Chapter 7.

Steam traps

We begin to see from our survey of a process and a power steam circuit that there are many points in both systems where condensate forms by the steam giving up its Specific enthalpy of evaporation; in transmission lines, where the Specific enthalpy of evaporation has been wasted; in process units, where the Specific enthalpy of evaporation has been put to good use (and sometimes some of the Specific enthalpy of water also); in power plant, where the presence of condensate can be a potential danger.

We have seen that superheat is wanted in one place and not in another; that steam pressures must be high here and low there.

We have seen that condensate from whatever source should be returned for boiler feed, or at least that its heat should be extracted from it.

We have seen that the automatic drain valve, known as a Steam trap, is the only efficient means by which this condensate can be taken away from where it is not wanted and helped on its way to where it will do most good.

2 Steam trap types

The duty of a steam trap – to discharge condensate while not permitting the escape of live steam – is common to all designs of trap; but there are several methods by which this can be done. The steam pressures at which steam traps must operate may be anywhere from vacuum to the highest in practical use. The quantity of condensate which steam traps have to discharge on different jobs may vary from a trickle to a flood. They may have to be suitable for saturated steam or for superheated steam. They may have to discharge condensate at steam temperature, as soon as it forms in the steam space; or they may have to discharge it below steam temperature, after it has given up some of its Specific enthalpy of water.

To suit these varied conditions so many different steam trap types have been produced, each having its own advantages and disadvantages, that the choice can be bewildering.

Nevertheless there are only three characteristics that differentiate the behaviour of steam and condensate as they arrive at the point where a steam trap has to be fitted.

Firstly, the density of steam and hot condensate is different; therefore a float can be used that will sink in steam and rise in water. This property gives rise to the range of mechanical steam traps.

Secondly, a temperature difference can be made between the steam and condensate if the two are separated, as the condensate will begin to lose its Specific enthalpy of water. From this property has sprung the range of thermostatic traps.

The third factor is a trifle more complicated. It is necessary to refer back to the very beginning of the book and Figure 1 (page 10), and the very end of the book and the Steam tables, because we must consider the phenomenon 'flash steam'.

Let us say that 1 kg of condensate at 400 kPa gauge pressure arrives at a point where it is to be discharged through a steam trap to atmospheric pressure. As water it occupies 0.001 m³ and has a Specific enthalpy of water of 641 kJ. As soon as the condensate passes through the valve of the trap and the pressure drops to atmospheric the Specific enthalpy of water must drop to 419 kJ. The surplus heat in our 1 kg of condensate, amounting to 222 kJ, is used up in evaporating some of the condensate into what is known as 'flash steam'. It needs 2257 kJ to make 1 kg of steam at atmospheric pressure: so this surplus will produce $\frac{222}{2257}$ kg of steam. Now 1 kg of steam at this pressure occupies 1.67 m³, so the surplus heat will produce $\dfrac{222 \times 1.67}{2257}$ m³ of steam = 0.164 m³. Flash steam, its formation and its uses, is discussed at various points in this book, here we are concerned only with it in relation to steam trap design.

If condensate is to be discharged at full steam temperature there will be a maximum of flash steam formed at the trap outlet. This will cause a maximum build-up of pressure due to the sudden local increase of volume. If the condensate temperature is cold there will be no build-up at all. Also if there is an artificial restriction to the condensate outflow these tendencies will be magnified.

The incidence of flash steam formation and the subsequent pressure build-up is the basis for the design of steam traps of the types known variously as Labyrinth, Impulse and Thermodynamic. While the subject is fresh in our minds we will consider them first.

Flash pressure traps

Labyrinth steam traps

Figure 13 shows a typical construction of a labyrinth trap. The design in its simple form is seldom used nowadays, but it is interesting to study.

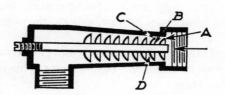

Figure 13

When steam is turned on, air is pushed past the clearance A to the first expansion chamber B, then through the clearance C to the chamber D and so on until it reaches the outlet. The pressure is dropped in each stage, but the air eventually gets away. Then comes condensate – at first this is cold, so that as the pressure is dropped in each expansion, it does not flash to steam, but is passed through as water. As the temperature increases a tendency to flash begins and the point at which this occurs depends on the relative clearances and expansion volumes. Labyrinth traps are adjustable. If the clearances are opened wide, both hot condensate and steam can pass. If the clearances are screwed up small, only comparatively cool condensate will pass. The trap is therefore set on the job – first it is opened wide so that steam blows, then it is closed down until the steam loss is just prevented. At this setting condensate will pass until its temperature is just so much below that of steam that flashing in the expansion chambers prevents the escape of more water.

If the steam pressure varies, then the setting is upset: a drop in pressure will allow steam to pass, a rise will cause condensate to be held up. A rise in the temperature of the condensate will also cause a hold up.

These traps generally discharge condensate continuously and at a temperature below that of the steam.

They have no moving parts whatever and their operation is directly controlled by the condensate pressure and temperature.

Partially to obviate the necessity of resetting the labyrinth position by hand, some traps of this general type include a bimetallic element that responds to variations in condensate temperature.

Impulse traps

Figure 14 shows an interesting variation of the labyrinth trap. The main valve E has a hole through it and an orifice A at the top. C is a thin piston disc on the valve body and it moves in the guide D. The guide is tapered, being wider at the top than at the bottom.

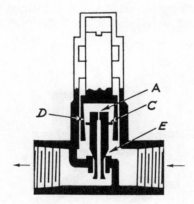

Figure 14

When steam is first turned on, the pressure acting under C lifts the valve so that air is passed out. Then comes water. This too passes out of the valve direct; water also passes round C into the chamber above the valve and is discharged through A. The clearance at C drops the pressure of water passing round so that the pressure below C is greater than the pressure above it.

As the condensate gets up to steam temperature the orifice A is choked with flash steam. A pressure is then set up above the valve which begins to fall on to the reduced taper in D. The valve is then open to suit hot condensate conditions.

If steam arrives, it passes comparatively easily round the reduced clearance C and drops the valve. If, instead of steam, cooler condensate arrives, the top flashing ceases and the valve lifts.

This type of trap is obviously very simple, but its correct operation does depend upon the maintenance of fine machining limits under arduous conditions.

Condensate is discharged continuously (through A, main valve shut) if the load is light, intermittently if the load is medium, and continuously if the load is heavy. The temperature is somewhat below that of steam.

Operating power is derived directly from the temperature and pressure of the steam.

Thermodynamic traps

Figure 15 shows an interesting, and very important, type of trap that relies at least partly on the formation of flash steam from condensate arriving at increasing pressure and temperature; this accounts for the 'thermo' beginning of the name. The 'dynamic' end exploits the Bernoulli theorem that in a moving fluid the sum of dynamic and static pressures is constant.

A in Figure 15 is a finely finished disc that is also a freely floating valve.

It mates against concentric seat rings C. When steam is first turned on, the disc A is raised by the pressure and air is discharged through the outlet passage B. Condensate follows, cold at first, and is discharged. As the condensate temperature and pressure rise so flash steam is formed under the disc and the velocity of this passing below the disc towards the outlet increases.

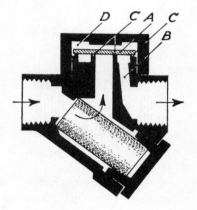

Figure 15

Here Bernoulli takes over. The increasing velocity lowers the pressure under the disc, so the disc is drawn towards the seat rings. However at the extreme circumference of the disc the velocity is reduced and the pressure builds up in the chamber D above the floating disc. At a point when the condensate temperature has approached that of steam the flash-produced pressure in D acting on the large area of the disc overcomes the inlet pressure acting on a small diameter. The disc A snaps shut against the rings C and prevents further flow.

Deprived of further flash steam, the pressure in the control chamber D falls and the inlet pressure once again opens the valve for the cycle to be repeated.

The length of time during which the trap remains shut depends on how quickly the control chamber pressure falls. Heat is lost through the top cap to the atmosphere and also through the body of the trap to the fluid at the trap inlet. If this is live steam the loss of heat from the control chamber will be less than if it is condensate which has cooled below steam temperature and the trap will cycle less frequently. Some traps have radial grooves or bleed passages machined in the disc to cause a leak from the control chamber D across the outer ring C to the outlet. This prevents the trap from staying closed for very long and can, under light load conditions, cause rapid wear.

If thermodynamic traps are installed in the open, cold winter conditions can cause the loss of heat from the top cap to be more rapid than is desirable and an insulating cover should be fitted to reduce it. In some traps the same effect is produced by jacketing the control chamber, using an additional cap and leading the incoming condensate through the space between the two caps. There is then a possibility of the trap working too slowly when used indoors on a heavy load and waterlogging the plant.

Since flash steam formation is greater with an increase in pressure, the pressure available to close the disc rises with the pressure available to open it and the trap is self-balancing both for pressure and for superheat. The disc is the only moving part, so there is nothing within the trap that can be damaged by extraneous forces such as a waterhammer. These traps can be made entirely in stainless steel, minimizing corrosion problems, and they can be frozen solid without coming to any harm. A significant development is the provision of three equally spaced outlet passages in place of the single passage B shown in Figure 15. This evens out the forces acting on the disc, preventing it from tilting about one edge and so reduces wear.

However, unfortunately for works engineers, no trap is suitable for every condition and this very useful thermodynamic trap is no exception. At pressures below some 35 to 55 kPa insufficient flash steam is available to operate the disc (the 'thermo' part). If the trap discharges against a back pressure and this is gradually increased, there will come a point when the dynamic effect is lost. This will vary with individual designs, and the makers' literature should be consulted for the maximum permissible back pressure.

The ability of a thermodynamic trap to pass air will depend on velocity. For example, when starting up, air will lift the disc and pass freely, to be followed by condensate in the normal way. Should its velocity happen, on occasions, to increase to the point at which the dynamic effect becomes great enough to seat the disc, the trap will close. But this generally happens at a higher pressure than it would with steam and often the trap will reopen quite soon because the air in the control chamber is warm and quickly loses heat and contracts, allowing the disc to lift.

To try and overcome air binding when starting up, some thermodynamic traps are fitted with a bimetal device arranged to hold the disc off its seat when cold, but to retract out of the way when hot. However should the bimetal stick due to dirt the disc will be prevented from seating and rapid wear will occur.

On jobs where a lot of air has to be discharged it may be necessary to fit a separate air vent in parallel with the trap.

Thermodynamic traps operate intermittently with a blast action and discharge condensate close to steam temperature.

Mechanical steam traps

This is the range of traps that operates by using the difference in density between steam and water. They are divided into open top bucket traps, inverted bucket traps and closed float traps.

There is one factor that affects all of these types, and we may as well explain it here to save repetition. The power needed to close the valve onto its seat comes from the buoyancy of the float or bucket. Once the valve is seated an additional force comes into play to hold it there due to the steam pressure acting on the area of the seat orifice. When the condensate level in the trap body falls, the float or bucket has to be heavy enough to unseat the valve against the steam pressure. Clearly there is a relationship between the maximum pressure up to which the trap will operate, the size of the discharge orifice and hence the trap capacity and the physical size of the trap body needed to house the float or bucket and any lever mechanism used to improve their mechanical advantage.

This is why mechanical steam traps are usually provided with a range of orifice sizes allowing greater capacities at the lower operating pressures and why the maximum pressure is reduced as the size of orifice is increased.

Open top bucket traps

Figure 16 shows the basic design of the open top bucket type of the mechanically operated group. Condensate from the equipment to be drained flows in at D and fills up the body of the trap, in which the bucket A is resting on the bottom. To the bucket A there is fitted a valve B which operates against a valve seat C. As condensate rises in the body of the trap the bucket floats until the valve is shut. Now at this stage it may be that no more condensate can get into the trap, although it wants to, because the top of the trap body is full of air which cannot

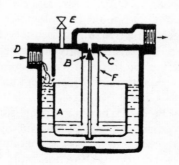

Figure 16

be displaced. To prevent this happening, traps of this type are fitted with a hand operated blow off valve E. If valve E is opened on starting any locked air will be discharged and condensate can continue to flow to the trap. Alternatively valve E can be replaced by an automatic valve that opens to release air, because air locked in the top of the trap will cause a drop in temperature that opens a thermostat in the valve. In one design a small hole is drilled in the discharge tube F which goes most of the way to obviate air-binding. The bucket cannot rise any higher, so water begins to overflow into it. As this continues the time comes when the bucket can no longer float. In sinking, it pulls the valve B off the seat C. Steam pressure then blows the condensate out of the bucket. The weight of the bucket is so designed that the bucket floats again before it is completely emptied. This leaves a water seal in the bottom which prevents the escape of steam.

The trap is now ready to begin the cycle again. The steam which fills the trap condenses, water enters, the bucket sinks and so it continues. But somebody must remember to shut the air release valve, unless by some means this can be done automatically, otherwise live steam will escape. It is also possible that air will find its way to the trap while the plant is running, having separated from the steam. This will cause the trap to air bind and the valve E will have to be opened again.

Traps of this type have an intermittent or blast discharge because no condensate is discharged while the bucket is filling. The condensate is at steam temperature.

Because of the relationship between bucket weight, maximum pressure and capacity explained at the beginning of this section, traps of the open top bucket type must be large if they are to handle large amounts of condensate at anything except low pressures or if they are to operate at high pressures and handle more than small amounts of condensate. Because of their bulk and the increased cost that this entails, open top bucket traps are no longer widely used, which is a pity, since their robust construction means that they are very reliable.

Float traps

A very important trap that, like the bucket traps, operates on the difference in density between steam and condensate, is the float trap. A closed, hollow, buoyant float, usually spherical in shape, operates the valve either directly or through a lever mechanism.

Figure 17 shows the construction of a trap of this type.

The trap does not need to be filled with water, or primed, before it will operate. When steam is first turned on, the float A is resting in its lowest position and the valve is closed. If air is driven along in front of the condensate, it cannot escape from the trap and some means for releasing it must be provided, such as the hand operated cock shown at the top of the body. The removal of this air will facilitate the collection of condensate in the trap body. The design is such that condensate does not begin to lift the float until the valve seat B is covered, thus providing a water seal to prevent the escape of live steam on light loads. After

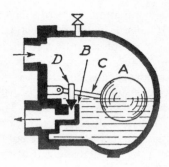

Figure 17

this level is reached any further addition of condensate will raise the float. This motion is passed through the float rod C to the valve D by a suitable arrangement of levers which increases the power of the float to lift the valve off its seat against the differential pressure. The amount of valve opening depends on the position of the float or the level of the condensate. As the condensate rate increases, so the level rises and opens the valve wider. A trap of the type shown discharges condensate continuously and at steam temperature.

The operating power to close the valve is provided by the weight of the float; the operating power required to open the valve, against the steam pressure acting on the valve area, is the buoyancy of the float multiplied by the system of levers. The capacity and pressure range of these traps is determined by the size of the float and the mechanical advantage of the system of levers. This sets a practical limit on the size of a single valve orifice that can be used beyond which the trap becomes excessively large and expensive.

One common way of overcoming this is to use a double seated valve of the type shown in Figure 18. By opposing the two valve clacks in this way on a single spindle some of the seating force caused by the differential pressure is cancelled out. However it must not be expected that this type of valve will give a tight shut off because of the difficulty of arranging for the two valve clacks to touch their seats simultaneously under all conditions of pressure and, therefore,

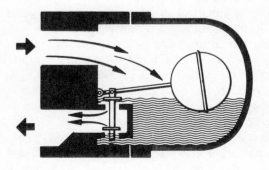

Figure 18

temperature. In practice this is not a disadvantage because this type of valve is only used where discharge capacities are very high and a tight shut off, therefore, is not needed.

A simple version of the float trap eliminates a separate valve and its associated levers, the float itself resting on the valve orifice in its lowest position and stopping the flow. With this arrangement the shut-off depends on the accuracy and cleanliness of the surface of the float and the force with which it seats is not multiplied by a lever mechanism.

The float trap shown in Figure 17 suffers from the disadvantage that air must be removed manually before it will work properly. Most modern float traps incorporate a mechanism for doing this automatically. A very common arrangement is to fit into the top of the float trap body an automatic air vent in the form of a balanced pressure trap element or a bimetal trap element, and a trap of this type is shown in Figure 19. Now, when steam is turned on and the condensate pushes air towards the trap, it passes out through the open valve of the automatic air vent. Then condensate reaches the trap and lifts the float, opening the valve. If the condensate rate is very heavy, the level may rise so that water is discharged through the air vent valve also. When the condensate rate falls and steam can reach the trap, the air vent element expands and shuts its valve. The exact operation of these elements is described later in this chapter. It is sufficient for the moment to know that they close off when surrounded by steam but open to the lower temperature of air or condensate. Because of this subsidiary valve, not only is air discharged when starting from cold, but also any accumulation of air is discharged when the plant is running. This is because a collection of air sufficient to cause air binding must be at a lower temperature than pure steam and so will cause the air vent element to contract and open the air valve.

Attempts have been made to combine the air vent with the main float operated valve. This is usually done by arranging for the float to work through a bimetal element, which holds the valve open when cold, but air discharge at low differential pressures may be hindered by the water seal covering the main seat.

Reference will be found in Chapter 3 (page 58) to a modification to the float trap to combat the problem of steam locking. This takes the form of a Steam Lock Release (SLR) and Figure 41 shows the arrangement. An adjustable

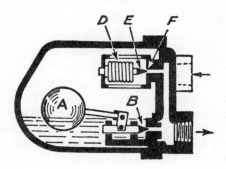

Figure 19

needle valve is incorporated into the trap and connects the steam space to the outlet.

Sometimes this needle valve is fitted instead of the automatic air vent because it will pass sufficient air to prevent air binding on start up. There are applications which call for both a Steam Lock Release and an air vent to discharge quickly quantities of air on start up and while the plant is running. Float traps are available fitted with both units which makes for a neat installation.

Inverted bucket traps

Figure 20 shows the basic design of a mechanical steam trap operated by the movement of an inverted bucket.

Some makers of these traps recommend that the trap be filled with water before starting up.

The action is as follows – assuming trap to be empty. When steam is turned on, the bucket A, which is open at the bottom, is lying on the bottom, and valve B to which it is attached, either direct or through levers, is pulled off the seat C. Any air which is present in the plant is expelled by steam pressure either round the bottom of the bucket and out through C, or through the small hole D in the top of the bucket and so out through C. Condensate enters and fills up the body and also the bucket, expelling remaining air through D. The valve B is still open and condensate is discharged. Then steam reaches the trap and passes up into the bucket.

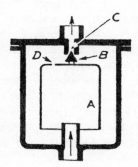

Figure 20

Some steam passes up through D to be lost, but most of it displaces the water from inside the bucket, so that the bucket floats and brings the valve B up to the seat C. If condensate is coming only very slowly to the trap, the steam escapes at a low rate through D and condenses in the water in the body – the water in the body being, however, very nearly at steam temperature. Condensate will gradually fill up the bucket, according to the rate at which it is reaching the trap. There will come a moment when the buoyancy of the bucket is lost, the bucket will then sink and pull the valve off its seat, permitting the condensate to be discharged. Any air which comes to the trap during the running period will collect in the bucket and pass slowly away through the hole D.

In the standard design, the larger D is the faster air will escape and the faster steam will pass; the smaller D is the slower steam will escape, but the slower air will be able to get away. In some designs there is an additional hole D in the bucket top, the opening of which is controlled by a simple thermostat. But since the trap is always full of water the small temperature difference to operate this thermostat does not permit it to have much power.

The valve of an inverted bucket trap is kept shut by the steam pressure and the power to open the valve is provided by the weight of the bucket. The design of the bucket must also be such that its buoyancy, when holding steam, can bring the valve up to the seat. As before, these two properties of the bucket determine the discharge capacity and operating pressure of the trap.

Inverted bucket traps discharge condensate intermittently and at steam temperature.

Thermostatic steam traps

At any given pressure saturated steam must be at one temperature and one temperature only. In condensing it forms water at steam temperature, but the water can and does begin giving up Specific enthalpy of water and loses temperature, although the pressure on the surface of it is still steam pressure. Thermostatic steam traps differentiate between water and steam because of this difference in temperature between the two.

Metallic expansion traps

Figure 21 shows the construction of the simplest form of thermostatic trap.

When steam is first turned on, any air in the plant is forced out. It passes up the metal tube A and out at the open valve B. Condensate follows and passes through. As the condensate becomes hotter, the metal rod expands and the seat B is brought closer to the valve C. At some definite temperature the rod has expanded sufficiently to close the valve. The position of the valve C can be altered by adjustment. In practice the valve is slacked back, so that even at steam temperature the expansion of the rod is not sufficient to bring B up to C. Steam

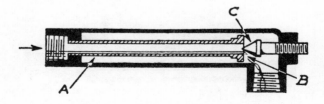

Figure 21

will blow. The valve C is then brought forward until the blow of live steam just disappears. The valve is locked in this position and the trap is ready for regular operation.

So long as the steam pressure in the plant remains constant the trap will operate satisfactorily. At some temperature just below steam temperature the trap will have shut; at any temperature below that it will be open. The colder the condensate, the greater the valve opening, so that on starting up the plant, when the condensate rate is greatest and the condensate coldest, the rate of discharge will be greatest. This is a good point. But should the steam pressure vary, the steam temperature also will vary. If the pressure rises, the trap will close too soon and hold up condensate; if the pressure falls, the trap will not have shut before the lower temperature steam reaches it and so it will waste steam. This is a bad point. The trap will open if it is cooled by an accumulation of air, which is a good point.

The amount of expansion of a metal per degree temperature difference is very small and to get sufficient valve movement the trap must be long and somewhat cumbersome – a length of a metre or more is required.

Several ingenious ways of overcoming this particular difficulty have been adopted. Basically they consist of the use of two metal rods with different coefficients of expansion linked to a third member carrying the valve. By a geometric link work it is possible to get a considerable magnification of movement in this third member.

Metallic expansion traps discharge condensate continuously and at a temperature which can be set to be anywhere below steam temperature.

The operating power of the trap is the difference in temperature between steam and condensate acting through the enormous power of the expansion of a metal. The discharge capacity is determined by the steam pressure and temperature and the amount of movement of the metal element.

Liquid expansion traps

Figure 22 shows the construction of a typical thermostatic trap in which the difference in temperature between steam and condensate causes the operation of a liquid filled thermostat – a liquid being used for the expansion medium instead of metal in order to obtain a greater valve movement per unit temperature difference and so a more compact design.

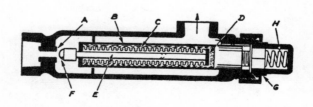

Figure 22

When steam is first turned on, air from the plant is expelled through the open valve A. This is followed by condensate, which also gets away. As the plant warms up, so the condensate gets hotter. The thermostatic element B is filled with some suitable liquid C which expands when heated. The liquid is sealed in the thermostat, but is in contact with a piston D which is free to move. On the piston rod E is fixed a valve F. Heat from the condensate is quickly transmitted to the liquid C and causes it to expand. This expansion pushes down the piston D, rod E and valve F bringing it nearer to the seat.

It must be particularly noted that in this type of trap the thermostatic element is on the outlet side of the valve and the temperature round the trap cannot be higher (except momentarily under superheat conditions) than 100 °C – unless the trap outlet is under back pressure, when the temperature can be the temperature of saturated steam corresponding to that pressure.

As the condensate before the trap approaches steam temperature, the valve F will be brought so close to the seat that only a trickle will pass – just sufficient to maintain the temperature of the liquid. It may even be that no condensate at all is forming. If steam should blow through the valve this will provide just that extra temperature to close the valve completely. Separated from its source of heat, the liquid will begin to contract and open the valve. Should only steam be still present the first whiff of steam will close the valve again. Should condensate have formed in the meanwhile, this will pass and, according to its temperature, cause the valve to take up an appropriate position. The condition just described is that associated with superheated or dry steam conditions and very light loading.

If the condensate rate is heavy, the water will be at a lower temperature, having been out of contact with the steam supply for a while. The valve will be correspondingly wider open.

Traps of this type have an adjustment G so that condensate can be passed out at a temperature suitable for the plant conditions. It must be remembered that the valve will shut at some temperature generally below 100 °C, but that the temperature at which condensate is formed is steam temperature. The plant may be such that it can use the Specific enthalpy of water, represented by this difference, to advantage. In which case the trap would be installed directly on the plant outlet and cooling of the condensate would take place in the plant itself. It may be a disadvantage to let this condensate lie, in which case the trap would be installed at a distance from the plant after a length of piping.

A fall in steam pressure will not cause this trap to blow steam, assuming the steam temperature is still above 100 °C. A rise in steam pressure, by raising the temperature of condensate formation, may bring the valve nearer to the seat and slow down the rate of discharge.

The spring H shown in Figure 22 is an overload safety spring. If the valve is moving up to close due to expansion of the liquid and a sudden high temperature gets through – due perhaps to superheat – the valve may shut and the oil still not have absorbed this extra heat – because of a time lag in conducting the heat to the oil. The oil must expand further, but it cannot push the piston down any more. So the thermostatic element moves bodily against the overload spring, which absorbs the movement and saves damage to the element.

These traps generally discharge condensate continuously, but may have an intermittent action on light loads. The temperature of the condensate is normally below atmospheric boiling point.

The power to open the valve is the steam pressure, the power to close the valve is liquid expansion derived from the condensate temperature. The capacity is determined by the steam pressure and condensate temperature and not by the power of the trap.

Balanced pressure thermostatic traps

We now come to a very important group of traps operated by what is known as a 'balanced pressure' thermostatic element. Figure 23 shows the construction of a typical trap of this type.

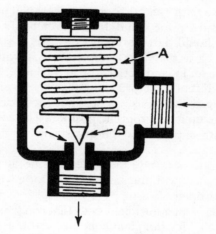

Figure 23

The thermostatic element A is a sealed vessel with a rigid metal top and bottom, but with side walls which will lengthen or shorten if the rigid ends are pulled apart or pushed together. The element is partly filled with a liquid, usually alcohol or a mixture of alcohol and water, having a boiling point lower than that of water. In some cases the boiling point of the liquid is reduced by filling the element under vacuum. The length of the element when cold is such that the valve B is off the seat C.

Figure 24 shows the vapour pressure – temperature curves of water and a mixture of water and volatile fluid suitable for use in the thermostatic element.

When steam is first turned on, air is discharged through the open valve orifice B which is carried on the floating end of the thermostatic element A – the top end of the element being rigidly fixed to the trap. Cold condensate enters and passes out. As the condensate warms up it transmits heat to the mixture in the element, which expands and pushes the valve C a little closer to the seat. At a temperature *t* (Figure 24) below the saturated steam temperature corresponding to the pressure at the trap, the mixture boils and begins to exert a vapour pressure. When the outside of the element is at steam pressure, the inside,

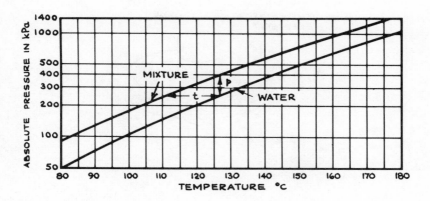

Figure 24

because of the temperature head, is at a pressure which is higher by the amount *p*. This excess pressure forces the valve down on the seat and closes the trap just before steam temperature is reached. Condensate is then held up in the trap until it has cooled to the amount *t* below steam temperature. At this point the vapour pressure in the element is less than the outside steam pressure so that the element returns to its original shortened length and the valve opens.

Since the graphs of water and element mixture are nearly parallel it does not matter what the steam pressure in the trap may be. At any temperature *t* below the saturated steam temperature the mixture will begin to boil and the valve move down. At any pressure there will always be an unbalanced force *p* holding the valve shut when steam is in the trap.

If superheated steam should reach a trap of this type, the superheat will boil the mixture and set up an internal pressure which is greater than *p*. This will disturb the operating principle and the trap will no longer follow the saturation curve. If the amount of superheat is excessive enough pressure may build up inside the element to fracture the flexible walls.

These traps often discharge condensate intermittently but, with some types and under certain conditions, the flow may be continuous.

The temperature at which condensate is discharged depends upon the mixture in the element. It will always be at a temperature *t* below steam temperature, but *t* may be anything between say 25 °C and 3 °C, according to the makers' design.

The power to close the valve is provided by the unbalanced pressure *p*, which again depends on the mixture in the element.

For many years, because the elements of balanced pressure thermostatic traps were made from thin walled bellows, usually of brass, they would not withstand waterhammer or corrosive condensate and were damaged by superheat. Modern materials and manufacturing techniques have gone a long way towards overcoming these difficulties. Figure 25 shows a very compact element fabricated from stainless steel, which resists both corrosion and a fair degree of waterhammer and is also strong enough to take a certain amount of superheat

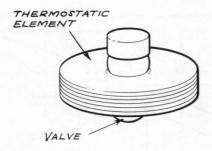

Figure 25

without excessive strain. These improvements have given a new lease of life to a trap which is very attractive because of its small size and ease of fitting and servicing.

Bimetallic thermostatic traps

It will have been noted that thermostatic traps using the expansion of a straight metal rod suffer because they must be so long to give the required valve movement, that the heat capacity of the rod makes them sluggish in responding to temperature changes and that they need adjusting to meet pressure variations – but they are rugged. Balanced pressure traps, on the contrary, are small, responsive to temperature changes (hence better than any other type for air venting) and self-adjusting to pressure variations – but the element can be damaged by waterhammer, corrosion and superheat. Various ingenious attempts have been made to combine the advantages of both types by the use of a bimetal thermostatic element. The results are frankly a compromise but because bimetal traps can readily be made from steel, will resist freezing and waterhammer and discharge condensate well below steam temperature so reducing flash steam, they are widely used in the petrochemical industry for such applications as tracer lines (see page 163).

It must be understood, as the name implies, that a bimetal strip consists of two dissimilar metals fabricated together to form one entity. The two metals have differing coefficients of expansion under heat. If they are of the same general composition, for example dissimilar stainless steels, their thermal activity will be small but their ability to resist corrosion will be great. If the metals are unlike in composition the reverse will apply.

This is the first compromise to be faced.

If an element made from bimetal is arranged to operate a valve on the inlet side of the seat orifice like the balanced pressure trap in Figure 23, there will be a wide difference between the opening and closing temperatures. This is because, when the trap is closing the flow will help the valve to shut, but before it can open again the bimetal will have to pull the valve off its seat against the pressure in the trap body. To exert sufficient force, the bimetal and, therefore, the condensate will have to cool down by a considerable amount.

It is for this reason that bimetal traps normally have the valve on the outlet side of the seat with the valve stem passing through the seat orifice to the bimetal element in the trap body. The pressure now helps the valve to open and any variation in steam pressure and temperature produces a corresponding variation in the forces acting on the valve.

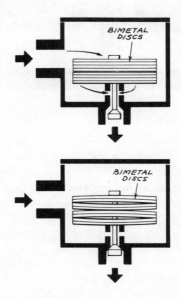

Figure 26

Figure 26 shows a trap constructed in this way with the element comprising a number of bimetal discs arranged in opposed pairs. When cold these discs are flat allowing the valve to open, but as they are heated up the pairs of discs deflect in opposite directions and the valve closes. Figure 27 shows the pressure versus temperature characteristic of this trap to be a straight line whereas the steam saturation line is curved.

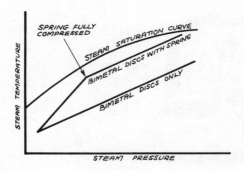

Figure 27

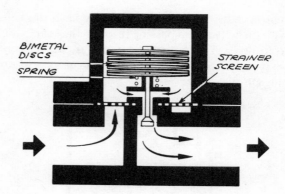

Figure 28

An improvement can be made to the bimetal disc trap by putting a spring between the discs and the trap body as shown in Figure 28. At lower operating pressures the spring compresses and absorbs some of the force of the bimetal but once it is fully compressed the trap works in the manner described above. The result is also shown in Figure 27.

The pressure/temperature characteristic now becomes two straight lines and the trap follows the steam curve more closely.

Even better results can be obtained by shaping the bimetal in various ways and also using a multi-stage valve arrangement. Figure 29 shows a trap with the element shaped like a multi-legged cross. As can be seen from Figure 30 the legs of the cross vary in length and breadth and they come into operation in sequence as the bimetal deflects under changing temperatures to produce a varying force on the valve. In this way a bimetal trap can be made to follow the steam saturation curve very closely.

Because of the mass of metal which has to be heated and cooled, bimetal traps tend to be slow in following variations in steam and condensate temperatures. Figure 29 shows how the leaves of the crosses are separated by bending the tips of the arms to allow quick temperature penetration.

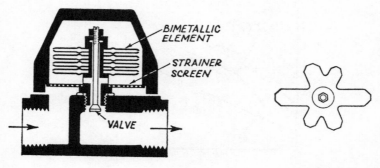

Figure 29

Figure 30

Bimetal traps are at their best when some use can be made of the Specific enthalpy of water in the condensate and at their worst when condensate must be discharged as soon as it forms. The temperature at which condensate is discharged can be altered by changing the position of the valve relative to the bimetal element. An adjusting nut is provided on the valve stem for this purpose.

Pilot operated steam traps

It is clear from what has gone before that there is a limit to the size of orifice that can be controlled directly by a float, balanced pressure, bimetal or other operating unit if the trap is to have a useful maximum working pressure without becoming excessively large in size. One way of overcoming this problem is to use the float or thermostatic element as a pilot to control the steam pressure as it acts on a piston which is then able to operate a very much bigger main valve.

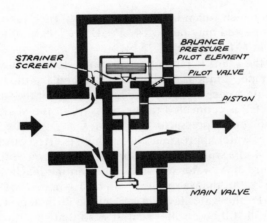

Figure 31

Figure 31 shows one form of pilot operated trap in which a small stainless steel balanced pressure element is used as the pilot member.

For very large capacities or where the operation of the plant is critical, the valve is sometimes operated electrically or pneumatically by a separate float level switch.

Drop legs

The simplest form of steam trap is not a separate piece of equipment, but an arrangement of piping.

Figure 32 shows a method of discharging condensate without losing steam which is of considerable value when steam pressures are very low. It is most commonly used when large amounts of condensate have to be discharged. It has however the great disadvantage that there is no way of getting air out of the plant.

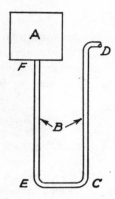

Figure 32

A is a vessel in which steam is being condensed. The pressure can never rise above 35 kPa gauge and may fall to 14 kPa. B is a length of pipe arranged as a U, the height from C to D being 3.75 m.

The first time the plant is put into operation, steam is turned on and air is blown out of the pipe. Condensate then forms and falls to the bottom sealing the U. More condensate comes along but it does not stand at the same height, in legs EF and CD. Leg EF is connected to the pressure in the vessel and leg CD to, shall we say, atmospheric pressure.

Now a column of water approximately 1 m high exerts a pressure of 10 kPa. A pressure in A of 14 kPa will therefore support 1.4 m of water in CD. If 14 kPa is the starting pressure in A, water will collect in B until it reaches the height D and begins to flow away, but the water in EF will be 1.4 m below D. As the pressure in A rises to 35 kPa the water level in EF will be pushed down until it is 3.5 m below D. There will still be a water seat at E so that steam cannot escape, but condensate is all the while flowing away from D. Unfortunately any air in the steam space of the vessel is now permanently trapped there, unless a hand-operated or automatic cock is fitted.

When steam is turned off A, it is possible that a vacuum may be formed which will cause the water to rise up the leg EF. It is probable that all the water will be pushed up EF by the atmospheric pressure at D. If the steam space will hold all the water, air will follow it up and the vacuum will be broken and some of the water will flow back into the U.

It is also possible that a vacuum may form in A due to rapid condensation of the steam when first turned on. These points do not affect the principle of the drop leg, but are a reminder that the lengths of leg EF and CD must be designed to suit the greatest possible pressure or vacuum conditions. The whole possibility of this simple arrangement is generally a matter of available height.

3 Steam trap installation

A steam trap has two functions:

(1) It must pass all the condensate that forms in the section of plant which it is draining.

(2) It must hold back any steam that reaches it.

There are certain faults in installation which make it impossible for the trap to carry out this work efficiently. They may be grouped according to that function of the trap with which they interfere.

Traps holding up condensate

It is one thing for condensate to form in a section of plant, but it is quite another for all that condensate to get to the trap.

Drainage point

Figure 33 shows a method of draining a steam main which ensures that all the water passing through that section of main does get to the trap. In this example the main is running horizontally (with, we hope, a fall of about 12 mm in 3 m in the direction of steam flow). As the steam passes over the drainage point the water must fall into the equal tee and so to the trap. But suppose this drainage point had been a 15 mm ($\frac{1}{2}''$) or 20 mm ($\frac{3}{4}''$) or even 25 mm (1″) connection from the bottom of perhaps a 150 mm (6″) or 200 mm (8″) main – there is no great

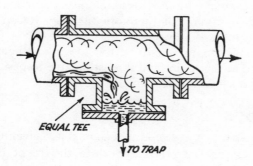

EQUAL TEE

TO TRAP

Figure 33

reason why all the water should suddenly go down that hole, since the steam is flowing past at a velocity of perhaps 40 metres a second.

A steam dryer or separator makes an ideal drain pocket (see page 23). Not only does it catch the condensate running along the bottom of the main but it also removes the water droplets suspended in the steam flow so greatly improving steam quality.

Recommended methods of draining plant are discussed in later chapters; the point to be remembered at this stage is that even the best steam trap cannot make condensate flow to it, and that if condensate is not in fact getting out of the trap it is only logical to find out whether the trap is in such a position that condensate can get to it.

Steam trap selection

Having decided the best point at which to drain the plant, the next problem is to find which of the many types of trap available is the correct one to use.

It will already have been noticed that a trap suitable for passing a certain amount of condensate at a certain pressure may be one of many types, it may be small or large, cheap or expensive, and pass condensate either at or below steam temperature.

Experience shows that all types of trap have their good points and their bad points, but most steam traps will work if the conditions are within their range of pressure and capacity. In advising about correct steam trapping, we are concerned, not so much with making sure that a steam trap will work, as with getting the greatest efficiency and output from the plant being drained. At first sight it may not be obvious how the difference between one trap installation and another can affect plant efficiency – but it does.

For example, some steam traps must condense steam inside themselves in order to operate. They may seem wasteful, but they have their special functions. Other traps enable good use to be made of some of the Specific enthalpy of water in the condensate. If you were to use a 'steam condenser' trap on a job which could make use of Specific enthalpy of water, you might be wasting as much as 12 % of the steam supplied to the unit. If the conditions were reversed and you had a 'Specific enthalpy of water user' trap in a place which needed a 'steam condenser' trap, you would most certainly reduce the output of the unit.

To give another example – some traps are noisy, particularly the intermittent discharge types. You would not therefore fit a noisy trap to drain hospital equipment, where silence is appreciated.

But whatever trap is chosen, it must be able to work at the maximum pressure which will be found at that point and it must be able to pass condensate at the maximum rate at which it forms.

Steam trap capacity

The amount of water which a steam trap can pass in a given time depends upon the difference in pressure across the valve orifice, the size of the valve orifice and the condensate temperature.

Because a unit of plant is fed with steam at, say, 700 kPa, it does not follow that the pressure at the trap is the same. When steam is first turned on and the unit is cold, the rate at which steam condenses is often so high that it may be quite an appreciable time before the pressure builds up in the steam space. Sometimes the steam supply pipe to the unit is too small and the heating surfaces can condense steam faster than it can reach them. This causes a greatly reduced pressure in the steam space.

It is not the pressure at the inlet to the plant, but the pressure at the inlet to the trap, which affects the trap capacity – and the two may not be the same.

The steam trap may be discharging condensate to the atmosphere. In such a case the differential pressure across the trap orifice is the gauge pressure at the trap inlet minus nothing.

The trap may be discharging into a condensate main in which there is back pressure (due perhaps to a leaking steam trap somewhere else on the line). In this case the differential pressure is the gauge pressure at the trap inlet minus the back pressure.

The condensate main after the trap may rise. Suppose, for example, it rises 6 m. A column of water 1 m high exerts a pressure of 9.8 kPa. So 6 m of water is pushing down with a pressure of 60 kPa at the trap outlet. This is back pressure on the trap and must be taken away from the trap inlet gauge pressure to find the differential pressure available. As the trap discharges, this column of water is set in motion and there is a frictional resistance to its flow. This friction depends on many factors, which on any given job are never known, so a simple and safe rule for our particular purpose is to say that every 1 m of lift causes a back pressure of 11 kPa and not 9.8 kPa. For example, the 6 m lift gives a back pressure of 66 kPa.

The trap may be discharging into a space which is below atmospheric pressure – for example, a condenser. In this case it is best to work in absolute pressures. For example, the trap inlet pressure may be 35 kPa gauge which is 136.3 kPa absolute and the outlet pressure 50 kPa absolute.

The differential pressure is $136.3 - 50 = 86.3$ kPa.

The next factor which determines the capacity of the trap is the valve orifice. It is so obvious that the larger the hole the greater the capacity, that we need not labour this point. But the length and shape of the orifice also affect the capacity, as also does the resistance to flow of the inlet and outlet passages in the trap body. This explains why different traps with the same orifice area can have different capacities.

It must be remembered that if a trap is ordered to work at, say, 620 kPa and the makers supply a trap with a valve seat of such an area that it is suitable for pressures up to, say, 700 kPa, you must not expect that trap to work if you put the pressure up to 800 kPa. It will not; it will shut down tight, just so long as the pressure is too high.

Even here we are considering differential pressures and not just trap inlet pressures. If that trap were discharging into a line carrying a back pressure of 140 kPa, the differential would only be 660 and the trap would still work.

If steam traps were always discharging cold water, the capacity of each could

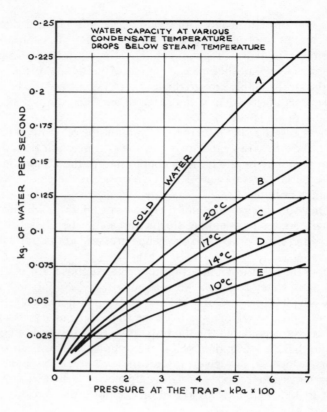

Figure 34

easily be decided and in a typical case could be something like curve A in Figure 34, which has been drawn from some actual test figures on a particular trap. In a description of labyrinth traps mention was made of flash steam and how it formed whenever very hot condensate was discharged to a lower pressure. This is exactly what happens when condensate, which is nearly at steam temperature and pressure, passes through a trap orifice to the very much lower pressure at the trap outlet. If follows, therefore, that in the valve orifice flash steam will begin to form. This flash steam will partly choke the hole and prevent the free flow of water.

Curves B, C, D and E in Figure 34 show the effect of this flash steam and how high temperature condensate lowers trap capacities.

It is, unfortunately, a common practice to choose steam traps according to the size of their inlet and outlet connections. These have no bearing at all on the discharge capacity of the trap. For example, should we decide to install an inverted bucket trap suitable for 275 kPa gauge, with 15 mm ($\frac{1}{2}''$) connections, we find, from makers' catalogues, that the following are offered:

		capacity at 275 *kPa*
15 mm ($\frac{1}{2}''$)	inverted bucket trap	0.095 kg/s
15 mm ($\frac{1}{2}''$)	inverted bucket trap	0.078 kg/s
15 mm ($\frac{1}{2}''$)	inverted bucket trap	0.034 kg/s
15 mm ($\frac{1}{2}''$)	inverted bucket trap	0.035 kg/s
15 mm ($\frac{1}{2}''$)	inverted bucket trap	0.059 kg/s
15 mm ($\frac{1}{2}''$)	inverted bucket trap	0.114 kg/s

If a steam trap has not sufficient discharge capacity to pass condensate at the maximum rate and at the pressure at which it is being formed, then condensate must be held up. One likely reason for the trap being too small is the practice of choosing traps on inlet size instead of on the rated capacity under working conditions.

Air binding

Assuming that we have chosen a trap which has a capacity large enough to discharge condensate at the greatest rate at which it forms, that the trap will work at the maximum steam pressure, and that it is so placed that condensate can freely reach it – we turn on steam – and nothing happens. If the trap is of the type which is closed when steam is off and no condensate is being formed, we may be fairly certain that it is full of air and that the arrangement of the piping to the trap is such that air cannot get out of the trap back to the steam space. Figure 35 shows just such an arrangement: the trap connected to the plant by a long length of small diameter horizontal pipe; condensate held up in the steam space and unable to flow down the pipe to the trap, because the air cannot get out. The reason for this locking is perhaps more apparent if we remember that there may be only a few centimetres of water head available to cause the displacement of the air.

There are several ways of preventing air binding. The connecting pipe can be so large that air can be displaced; but the outlet connection from the steam space must also be large enough to allow of the double flow. Remember, however, that this long pipe is full of steam most of the time and that it is condensing, probably to no useful purpose – the larger the pipe, the larger the steam loss.

Figure 36 shows another way of preventing air binding of the trap. The trap is brought nearer to the unit (to save steam) and a balance pipe is taken from the

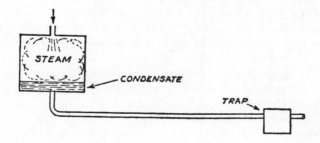

Figure 35

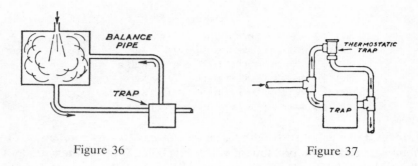

Figure 36   Figure 37

top of it back to the steam space. The disadvantage of this method is that air goes round and round and is never released from the steam plant (see Chapter 4).

A third method is to fit a hand-operated air vent on the trap. The vent must be opened on starting and must be closed when running. (Who is going to close it?) Since air accumulates in the steam space even under running conditions, the trap may air-bind again. If the outlet from the trap is not visible, nobody will know until the steam space once more waterlogs. It is not uncommon for the air vent of a trap to be left just cracked to get over this – and so steam is wasted.

Figure 37 shows a fourth way out of the trouble. A balanced pressure thermostatic trap will always discharge air and will close when steam reaches the element. If such a trap is fitted as an automatic by-pass round the main trap, the trouble of air-binding and consequent waterlogging cannot arise.

Steam locking

Consider Figure 35 again. Let us assume that the trap is fitted with a hand air vent, that the air has been blown out and the vent has been shut again. Condensate is being discharged satisfactorily and all is well. After a few minutes, when everything is hot, we begin to notice that the trap is shut for quite a while between discharges (intermittent action type) or that the flow has fallen off until nothing more is coming out (continuous discharge type). We may think that it is because no condensate is being formed. If the air cock on the trap is opened steam alone comes out for a moment until suddenly the trap begins to discharge condensate as fast as it can. These are typical symptoms of 'steam locking'.

The trap in Figure 35, if it is a good trap, will not only open to pass any condensate which reaches it, but it will close to steam. After the trap has closed to steam, all that long horizontal pipe may be momentarily full of steam, right back to the unit. Condensate which forms in the steam space cannot get down to the trap unless it can displace the steam, or unless the trap can be made to pass out the locked steam. Open the air cock on the trap, as just described, let this locked steam out and allow condensate to reach the trap.

The prevalence of steam locking is seldom realized. It is probably the most common cause of erratic steam trap working. If the trap is discharging into a closed condensate system it may probably never be noticed, because in time the steam in the connecting pipe will condense and the trap will operate again.

Steam locking is a particularly evil complaint, because it is at its worst where most care has been taken. If a trap is leaking steam, steam locking cannot occur. The better the trap, the worse the locking. If the connecting pipe has been well-lagged, to save steam loss, the locked steam will take longer to condense.

It is obvious that steam locking is not unlike air binding, but the cure for it is not necessarily the same. The simplest cure is to bring the trap as near as possible to the unit being drained. This will generally reduce to a negligible amount the time taken for any locked steam to condense. If the trap is below the unit, then the addition of a balance pipe as shown in Figure 36 will still further help.

Unfortunately the worst cases of steam locking do not occur in such simple circumstances. Figures 38 and 39 show two examples of bad steam locking.

Figure 38 shows the drain arrangement of a tilting jacketed pan. Steam enters through a trunnion at A and passes down a cored passage to be admitted to the steam space at B. Condensate drains out at C and is forced up to the outlet trunnion D through another cored passage and so to the trap at E. Whenever the outlet C is uncovered of water, steam passes up CD and so to the trap. No more water can be discharged until the steam in CD and DE is dispersed. However short DE is made, there is steam locked in CD and no balance pipe can be fitted. To make matters worse, the steam in CD can only condense slowly because the cored passage is kept hot by steam in the jacket.

Figure 39 shows one type of drain arrangement of a drying cylinder. Condensate collects in the bottom of the cylinder and is discharged through a syphon pipe AB, through a trunnion at B and down BC to the trap. Conditions here are similar to those described in the pan but they are if anything worse. The actual drain point at A in Figure 39 is not so good as at C in Figure 38. The syphon pipe in the drying cylinder is generally longer than that in the pan and it is completely surrounded by live steam.

In neither of these cases can steam locking be cured by fitting the trap close to the job. Neither can balance pipes be arranged. It serves no purpose to increase the size of the pipe from the trunnion to the trap, because the serious locking is in the syphon pipe itself. Increasing the size of the syphon pipe makes locking worse, not better. A thermostatic trap will cure air binding, but not steam locking, because steam will close the trap although air will open it.

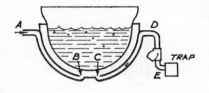

Figure 38

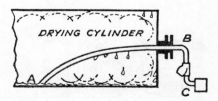

Figure 39

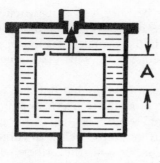

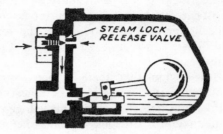

Figure 40   Figure 41

The only way of curing steam locking in syphon drainage jobs is to provide means of dissipating the locked steam. In an inverted bucket trap there is such a leak, through the small hole in the top of the bucket. But it must be remembered that unless this hole is kept small, the trap will be wasteful under normal conditions; also the pressure available to push the locked steam through the hole is only A centimetres of water, Figure 40.

The steam trap used can be fitted with an external by-pass, which will have to be kept permanently open. This will cure steam locking, but is a potential source of steam loss, if the operation of the by-pass is left to any Tom, Dick or Harry. Incidentally, it is probable that most of the by-passes which are fitted round steam traps are used to cure steam locking, although the existence of the steam lock has never been suspected. It has been found, from experience, that 'the trap works better that way'.

The most satisfactory method is to use a trap fitted with a steam lock release. Figure 41 shows such a design. An adjustable needle valve is incorporated in the trap which connects the steam space to the outlet. The adjustment should be arranged so that it can be locked. The initial adjustment must be made so that the trap does not blow steam, neither does it lock and go out of operation. It is easier to check this action in a closed float trap with a continuous discharge than with an intermittent discharge trap.

If the condensate is being returned through a closed system, the setting of the steam lock release can be made easy if a sight glass is fitted after the trap. Figures 42 and 43 show two types of sight glass. A look through the glass should show at once whether condensate or steam is passing or whether nothing at all is happening.

Figure 42   Figure 43

The first thought that arises is that such an arrangement must also be wasting steam. It is, of course. But it is only wasting waste steam. As soon as steam enters the syphon pipe, or the connecting pipe to the trap, it has already been wasted, because it can do no useful work in the steam space. If it is left in this pipe it is doing genuine harm by slowing down the process. It is therefore a saving to waste this particular pipeful of steam.

Group trapping

Figure 44 shows a condensate drainage arrangement which is not uncommon. Three steam heated units – they may be separate units, or three separate parts of one machine – discharge condensate into a common pipe, which leads to one steam trap. The layout is one which causes condensate to be held up and decreases output. Let us assume that each unit is fed with steam at the same pressure and that they are all the same size and doing the same work. A batch of raw material is put into A to be heated; B was started up just before, and the temperature is coming up; C was the first to go on and the stuff is hot. Because A is cold the temperature head across the walls to the stuff is a maximum and condensation is rapid; the pressure drop in A will be comparatively high.

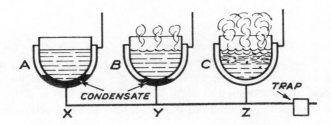

Figure 44

Because B is hotter, the condensation rate is less than in A and the pressure drop less. In C there is little condensation and little pressure drop. Therefore, although the inlet pressure to the three units is the same, the pressure at X, Y and Z will be different. There will be a higher pressure at Z than at X. The condensate forming in A – and there is a lot of it – is going to find it difficult to flow from X to Z because it will have to flow, so to speak, uphill. If there is a very long pipe leading from A to the point X there might be some chance of it getting away, due to static head, were it not for one other point.

Not only is Z at a high pressure, but there is little condensate being formed at C. It is certain that steam from C will follow this condensate to the trap and cause the trap to shut. The trap is now steam locked, in addition to the pressure complication, and the condensate at X has another reason for not getting to the trap.

These troubles will not arise should the trap be leaking steam sufficiently to lower the pressure in the common line so that condensate will flow even from the most heavily loaded unit.

There will not be a permanent hold up of condensate from A, but the temporary condition occurs just at the time when the condensation rate is greatest and it is most important to get the water away. The geographical position of the pans does not affect the issue. For example, when C is being started, condensate will be held up by the higher pressure arising from the lower loading of either B or A.

This trouble cannot be cured by fitting a check valve after each unit. A check at X, in the first example, would be held shut by the higher pressure from Z and no water would get away.

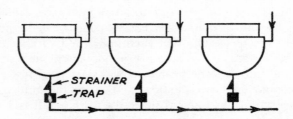

Figure 45

The correct procedure to ensure the quickest possible heating up of each unit is to fit a smaller steam trap at the outlet from each unit, as shown in Figure 45. The outlet from each trap can be joined to a common main with no trouble ensuing, provided, of course, that there is not a back pressure in the main which, due to other causes, is greater than the lowest pressure at any trap inlet.

Traps blowing steam

The second function of a steam trap is to ensure that steam shall not be blown out with the condensate.

There are quite a number of factors which will cause a trap to blow steam.

Dirt

When steam is first turned on to a new installation, it is remarkable to see what a strange assortment of foreign matter is swept down the line. Casting sand is most common, packing and jointing and swarf, solder and weld metal are usual, nuts and bolts and small spanners and even sparrows are not unknown. It is a good practice to blow steam through a new job before the steam traps are finally connected. All this rubbish, if left in the line, will finally reach the steam trap, that is, such of it that does not cause reducing valves to stick and meters to go out of action on the way. Unfortunately it may take months before this dirt comes to the trap, even when the pipes have been blown through. Then the steam may be clean for a while until another trouble starts – pipe scale. Pieces of scale become detached from the piping and pass through the system to the traps, or reducing valves, or meters.

However large the trap, or whatever type it may be, the time will come when a bit of dirt will be carried in the water flow to the valve orifice. It may be carried out and do no harm. But the orifice in a steam trap is small and it is much more likely that the dirt will be jammed on the seat and the valve will be unable to close, so that the trap will blow steam. If the trap is discharging to a closed system, this steam leak may not be noticed for quite a while. When it is finally discovered and that particular trap isolated, it will probably be found that the seat has been cut by the steam and that it must be replaced or ground in.

When you consider that it needs a hole only 1.5 mm in diameter, at a steam pressure of 700 kPa, to leak steam equivalent to 5 tonnes of coal a year, you will realize how expensive dirt in a steam system can be.

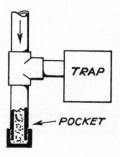

Figure 46

Figure 46 shows a dirt pocket arranged before a steam trap. This is a very common way of trying to prevent dirt getting to the trap. It is very simple, but unfortunately not very effective in practice. If there really is all this dirt that we have mentioned, it is obvious that the pocket will in time fill up. And nobody ever seems to clean dirt pockets. Secondly, the dirt does not always fall into the pocket; the condensate flow carries the lighter fibrous materials and the small stuff round the corner into the trap. Thirdly, the sudden turning on of steam may disturb all the dirt that has settled out and carry the whole pocketful into the trap.

The most satisfactory way of preventing loss due to dirt is to fit a pipe strainer before each reducing valve, meter or steam trap. Figures 47 and 48 show two types of small strainer that are simple, cheap and effective. It must however be stressed that strainers should be cleaned at intervals, otherwise they will pack solid and throttle the flow of condensate. It is as well to see that the straining area is large and that the holes in the screen are no smaller than they need be for the efficient working of the unit which they are protecting. Some traps have a strainer screen fitted into the body and this is convenient and satisfactory when the screen is of adequate size and can easily be removed for cleaning.

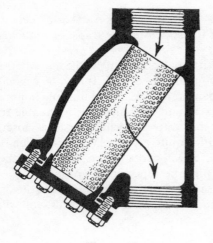

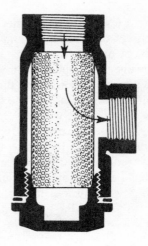

Figure 47   Figure 48

Corrosion

Corrosion in a steam system can affect traps in two ways; by attacking the traps, damaging the bodies and working parts and by attacking the pipework and fittings of the steam and condensate system so that rust and scale are formed and carried into the traps, interfering with their operation.

The major cause of corrosion is incorrect feed-water treatment or even no treatment at all. The result may be the formation of carbon dioxide gas and free oxygen which will react with certain metals in the presence of condensate and corrode them away. Or priming and foaming may take place in the boiler, so that boiler water containing impurities and feed treatment compounds is carried over into the steam system which may be attacked.

Sometimes the correct feed treatment is used but it is wrongly applied and this too can cause trouble. Dosing at infrequent intervals with a large quantity of chemicals is a case in point.

With the increasing use of packaged boilers having a high duty for their size, correct feed water treatment is of the greatest importance to ensure good quality steam which will not corrode the system.

Condensate may also become corrosive due to contamination by chemicals used in the process plant. Certain processes – for example, open vulcanizing – may demand that live steam is injected into raw material from which corrosive matter enters the condensate, or live steam may be injected into a corrosive liquid. If on such plants steam is shut off by a main (or a section) stop valve, there will be a vacuum formed between the valve and the liquid. Some liquid may be drawn up into the main and will find its way down other branches to other equipment. After steam is turned on there may be mysterious corrosion of the steam traps on these other jobs. The cure for this particular trouble is to fit a good non-return valve as a vacuum breaker on the line to the corrosive liquid tank.

Sometimes there may be steam heated pipe coils in corrosive liquid and a small leak in the coil. This may not matter when steam is on, but when the steam is turned off, the liquid may be drawn through the leak into the coil and in due course pass down to the steam trap.

Since stainless steels became freely available they have been increasingly used to enable the working parts of certain types of steam traps to resist most common forms of corrosion. If the corrosive condition is a natural result of the process such traps should be used. But all parts of the steam and condensate system, not only steam traps, will be affected, so that if the corrosive conditions can be eliminated at source, that is the sensible way out of this particular trouble.

An interesting development now widely used, which is aimed at preventing corrosion in steam systems, is the introduction of small quantities of filming amines into the steam.

Filming amines are organic chemicals derived from animal fat which form an extremely thin layer about one molecule thick on the inside wall of any pipe on which the steam condenses or which is wetted by condensate. This amine layer prevents the corrosive carbon dioxide/oxygen/water mixture from coming into contact with the metal of the pipe and so prevents corrosive attack.

The amines are either dissolved in the boiler feed water or injected into the steam when it leaves the boiler and are carried to all parts of the system by the steam so that the layer on the pipes is constantly reformed and kept in being. The amount of amine required is very small, being of the order of 1 to 5 parts per million in the steam.

Care must be taken when first introducing amines because they strip all the scale and dirt off the pipe walls so as to get down to the bare metal. All strainers must be inspected very frequently until the amount of dirt coming over falls away.

Filming amines are also said to improve heat transfer in the process plant by promoting dropwise condensation of the steam on the heating surface.

Care should be taken if the steam comes into direct contact with food or materials to be sterilized.

Waterhammer

A steam main should if possible be erected so that it has a continuous fall in the direction of flow and it should be so supported that it cannot sag. If this is not done, there is a danger of waterhammer.

Figure 49 shows a main that has sagged between hangers. When steam is on the line, this dip will form a natural collecting point for water (Figure 50). The

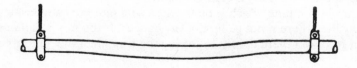

Figure 49

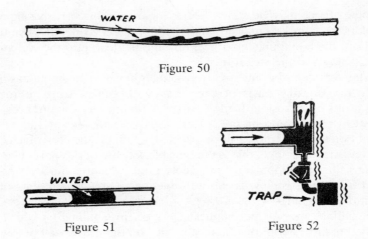

Figure 50

Figure 51   Figure 52

steam will be flowing over the low point at, say, 40 metres a second. This velocity will cause ripples on the water; the steam passage will be restricted; finally the whole pocket of water is picked up by the steam and carried forward in a solid column at 40 metres a second (Figure 51) to some point down the line where there may be a change of direction and perhaps a steam trap (Figure 52). The water is brought to a sudden halt at this point and the energy, which it has by virtue of its movement (Kinetic energy), is suddenly converted into pressure energy. This sudden pressure may do no more than give the trap mechanism a jolt, if it is a thermodynamic or bimetallic trap, but if it is a float trap, it may possibly collapse the float, or if it is a balanced pressure thermostatic trap, it may ruin the element.

The steam trap is not the only thing which may be damaged by waterhammer. Reducing valves and meters will certainly suffer and this is one common cause of leaking joints.

If some waterhammer is inevitable then use a robust trap such as a thermodynamic or inverted bucket type which will stand up to the conditions.

The cure for waterhammer is to get rid of the cause. Re-align the pipe if possible. If there must be a low point in it (to avoid a joist perhaps), then drain the low point with another steam trap.

Frost

This surely need be only a reminder that a steam trap may freeze when steam is turned off and the weather is cold enough.

If the trap is of a kind which is open when cold and the condensate can drain freely away then there is not generally any danger. If the trap is full of water and shut when cold or if there is a lift following the trap, then the matter needs more care.

Some thermodynamic and bimetallic traps are not damaged even when frozen solid and these are generally the best answer to the freezing problem.

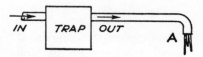

Figure 53

Lagging the trap well with a proper waterproof covering may also prevent damage unless the cold spell is prolonged. Be sure, however, that the trap is one which will continue to operate when the escape of heat is prevented. Lagging can also make maintenance more difficult.

An unsuspected reason for freezing is shown in Figure 53. If the trap is discharging to atmosphere and the cut off is not clean it is very easy for dribbles of water to freeze at A. If ice builds up at this point it may choke the outlet and cause the trap to freeze up, even when steam is still on. This applies equally to a trap which is wide open when cold.

If the condensate from the trap has to rise after the outlet, any type of trap may freeze when steam is off, because the system cannot be self-draining.

In very cold winters thousands of steam traps are ruined by frost damage so the matter is worth some thought.

Loss of prime (inverted bucket trap)

The inlet to the bucket chamber of an inverted bucket must be from the bottom and the chamber must be full of water for the bucket to float in. Should this water be lost for any reason, the trap is said to have lost its prime and it will blow steam.

Superheat in the trap may cause loss of prime by evaporating the water and setting up an excess pressure which would blow the water back out of the trap. A check valve should be installed on the inlet so that the water cannot be forced out.

A sudden pressure drop in the line may also cause loss of prime due to the water in the trap flashing into steam. A check valve on the inlet will also prevent this.

If the trap is to be installed above the unit being drained (see Figure 60) it is possible for the water to run back by gravity – again an inlet check valve is required.

If the trap must be fitted with a by-pass for some reason, care must be taken that the by-pass should not be below the level of the trap, or the prime will be lost when the by-pass valve is opened. Also, if a test cock is fitted on the inlet side of the valve, this should be arranged so that the prime is not blown out when the cock is opened.

Lifting condensate

Chapter 1 shows how important it is that all condensate should be returned for boiler feed if this is at all possible. Very often the feed tank is at a higher level than many of the steam traps. Often too, even when the feed tank is lower, it is essential that the pipe carrying condensate should be at a high level so as to clear obstacles. We will first consider lifting direct through the steam trap, although this is far from being the best practice.

First of all it must be made quite clear that it is not the steam trap which lifts the condensate. It is the steam pressure.

We stated, on page 53, that 9.8 kPa would support a column of water 1 m high. We further said that if this column of water were in motion there would be a friction loss due to its movement. So that, as a simple rule, we can say that a pressure of 11 kPa will keep moving a column of water 1 m high.

If, therefore, we must lift condensate 6 m, we need a steam pressure of 66 kPa to do it.

Whenever possible a layout for lifting condensate should be as shown in Figure 54. The trap is shown at the bottom of the lift and close to the unit being drained, to minimize steam locking; it is preceded by a strainer, to prevent dirt troubles; it is followed by a check valve. The check valve has two functions. First it will tend to prevent condensate running back down the rising leg when steam is turned off. This condensate would get back into the unit if the steam trap were of the type which is open when cold and if the volume of the rising pipe were greater than the volume of the steam trap body.

Should the steam be shut off for a long time – for example, a heating system in summer – condensate lying in the steam space may set up corrosion on the water line. Unfortunately, check valves are seldom quite tight and, in time, all the water from the rising leg will have dripped back. The simplest way to avoid this trouble is to drain the system. This can be done by a blow down cock on the strainer cap (Figure 55), an arrangement which has the added merit of ensuring a clean-out of the strainer.

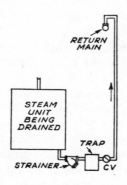

Figure 54

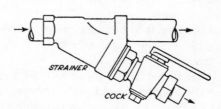

Figure 55

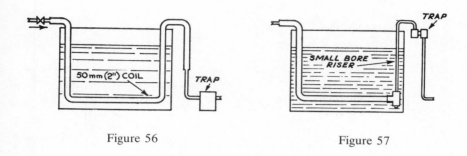

Figure 56   Figure 57

The check valve after the trap should, however, hold back condensate during a short shut down. Its second purpose is to isolate the steam trap from any back pressure which there may be in the return line and so make maintenance work on the steam trap easier.

It should be noted that the rising pipe goes into the top of the common main and not into the bottom. This is always advisable.

It is not always possible to fit the steam trap at the bottom of the lift. Figure 56 shows such a case and also shows a very common and very bad steam trap installation. Liquid is heated in a vat by a coil of, say, 50 mm (2″) pipe. The outlet has to come up over the side because of the type of vat construction. The steam pipe is perhaps 25 mm (1″), and the 50 mm (2″) pipe starts at the inlet valve, goes down the side, along the bottom, up the other side and is reduced somewhere before the trap. The first time that the unit is put into operation, incoming steam forces out the air from the pipe (if it can); the steam condenses and the condensate lies in the coil; steam passes over the condensate, up the rising pipe and keeps the trap shut. No condensate can begin to move from the coil until the steam is shut off from the rising pipe, and this cannot happen until the coil is, at one point at least, filled with water. Even then the condensate flow will not start at once, but must wait until the steam locked in the outlet loop is condensed or dissipated. Steam pressure then pushes some of the condensate out of the coil; but not all of it, because, as soon as the water seal is broken, steam again gets up the rising pipe, breaks the syphon, and shuts the trap. This vat is being heated most of the time by hot water and not by steam.

Figure 57 shows a much better way of doing the job. The end of the 50 mm (2″) coil is terminated as in Figure 58. This provides a small water seal in which the first condensate to form in the coil collects, so sealing the rising pipe before the coil even begins to waterlog. The outlet is of small diameter, which not only reduces the volume of locked steam, but makes it easier for the water column to be maintained without steam bubbling through, as it can do in an unrestricted large bore pipe. The trap is fitted as close as possible to the job and is preceded by a strainer.

Unfortunately such a layout is not always possible. The coil may be of some special material to resist corrosion and no joints below the surface are permissible. Figure 59 shows the way out of this particular difficulty. The end of the coil should be formed with a slight dip – if at all possible – and the angle at

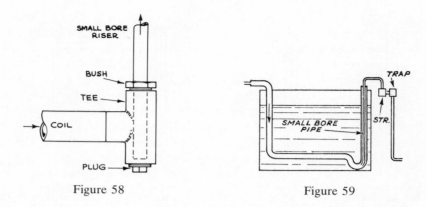

Figure 58   Figure 59

the rise made as sharp as possible. At some point above the liquid level, a small bore pipe is inserted in the large riser (the joint being made steam tight, of course) and pushed down as far as possible into the dip.

Similar conditions to the coil in the tank may arise whenever it is necessary to lift condensate and to fit the trap at the top of the lift. Figure 60 shows a simple problem and the wrong installation. As condensate begins to form in this system, it must lie in the pipe AB – and perhaps even in the steam space – while steam passes over it and keeps the trap shut. This will go on until water has sealed the pipe and until the locked steam in BC is dissipated. Since AB was full even before the steam supply to BC was cut off, the condensate which is still forming must be backing up in the steam space while the steam in BC is condensed or passed out.

Figure 61 shows the best layout for this set of conditions. Start with a strainer. It is probably more accessible for cleaning if low down and it will protect the check valve as well as the trap. The check valve is to prevent water from running back during a shut off; it may or may not be thought necessary. Then comes the Figure 58 arrangement to seal off the steam in the rising leg at the earliest moment. The rising leg is of the smallest diameter which is required to pass the peak rate of condensate. The exact method of connecting to the trap is important

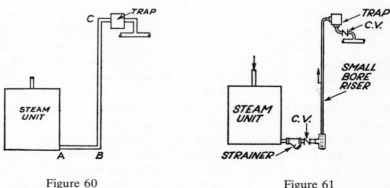

Figure 60   Figure 61

and depends on the type of trap. After the trap there is a check valve to isolate it from any back pressure in the condensate main during maintenance work.

Regarding the top connection to the trap: if the trap is any one of the mechanical types except the inverted bucket, there is nothing special to be done, just connect up the rising pipe in the simplest way. If the trap is of the inverted bucket type, a check valve must be fitted just before it to prevent the water in the trap from running back down the rising pipe. This loss of water would cause the bucket to sink and the trap to be open to pass steam. If the trap is of the thermostatic type, the rising pipe should be connected up as shown in Figure 62. This will give a sharper operation of the thermostatic element.

Unless the trap chosen for fitting at the top of the lift is one which cannot steam lock, even the arrangement shown in Figure 61 will not be quite so satisfactory as when the trap is at the bottom; although it may be that the efficiency of the unit will not suffer as a result of temporary steam locking. A radiator would not, for example.

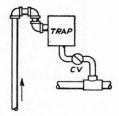

Figure 62

Pumping traps

Although technically possible, when the steam pressure is high enough in relation to the lift, and although sometimes inevitable, it is nevertheless better in practice not to lift condensate direct through the steam traps. Condensate should

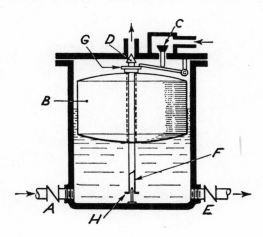

Figure 63

be allowed to gravitate naturally to a conveniently placed receiver, or receivers, from which it can be raised to an overhead line or tank by a pumping trap or automatic pump as it is perhaps more correctly called.

Figure 63 shows a typical construction of a pumping trap. It is installed so that condensate drains by gravity through the inlet check valve A into the body of the trap. As the water level rises it lifts the float B which comes up, guided by the exhaust valve rod F, until it meets a collar G, and starts to lift the rod. This opens the valve C, through a lever, allowing steam or compressed air to enter the body and build up sufficient pressure to close the exhaust valve D. The pressure then expels the water through the outlet check valve E to a higher level and the float falls. At the bottom of its travel the float meets another collar H on the rod F, which now moves down and opens the exhaust valve D, at the same time closing the valve C. The steam or compressed air above the float is vented through the exhaust valve and more condensate enters at A and the cycle is repeated.

The correct installation of the pumping trap on a condensate lifting job is a matter of supreme importance and it is recommended that Figure 64 is carefully followed.

Condensate drains by gravity from the steam traps to the tank or receiver of large bore piping, or some similar arrangement. The capacity of the receiver should be not less than twice that of the pump. The receiver should be vented, and, if this is likely to result in any great loss of flash, the vent can be taken in to the top of the overhead main to which the pump is lifting. But in such a case it is essential that the main should not be running full and if it carries any back pressure the pump manufacturer should be told, as it affects a detail of pump design. Loss from the pump exhaust is insignificant as the total steam consumption of these pumping traps is only of the order of 0.0006 kg/s.

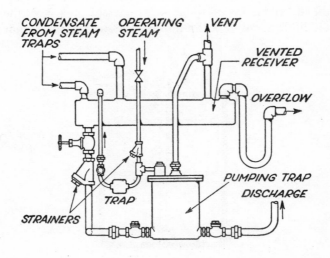

Figure 64

By using a pumping trap instead of lifting condensate direct through the steam traps maintenance is made easier, waterhammer dangers are avoided and the plant heats up much quicker from cold.

A pumping trap can sometimes be used to drain condensate from the steam space of a vessel under vacuum.

Vacuum — pressure drainage

It is sometimes necessary to heat substances that form heavy deposits on the heat transfer surfaces of heat exchangers, causing the rate of heating to fall off quickly. So that the heat exchanger can operate for a reasonable time without cleaning, it is usual to provide sufficient heating surface to give the necessary output even though it is partly fouled up. This means that when it is clean, the steam pressure has to be reduced, probably below atmospheric pressure, to prevent overheating. Then, as fouling takes place, the pressure is steadily increased up to the maximum, which can be well above atmospheric pressure, at which point the heat exchanger is taken out of service and cleaned.

This method of working obviously creates problems with condensate removal when there is a vacuum in the steam space. If a steam trap is fitted in the usual way it will handle the condensate when there is a positive pressure differential across it, but when a vacuum forms in the steam space waterlogging will take place. Condensate will build up, flooding some of the temporarily unwanted heating surface, until there is sufficient static head to balance the vacuum and the resistance to flow of the trap, when it will be discharged. Apart from the likelihood of corrosion occurring at the water line inside the heat exchanger, experience shows that this arrangement can cause waterhammer when the steam valve is opened, and sudden surges in temperature of the material being heated as condensate is discharged, exposing heating surface to full steam temperature. In addition it may not always be possible to provide sufficient static head above the trap, which must be big enough to pass the required amount of condensate with quite a small differential pressure.

An improvement can be made by fitting a vacuum breaker to the steam space so that when the pressure tries to drop below atmospheric, air is bled into the heat exchanger.

This prevents waterlogging and the mixture of air and steam which results has a lower temperature than pure steam (see Chapter 4) so giving the necessary reduced heat output. Although this arrangement allows automatic discharge of condensate under all conditions, there is still the possibility of corrosion because of the high concentration of air inside the heat exchanger. Special materials may be used to overcome this.

It is, of course, possible to fit a vacuum pump on the discharge side of the trap so that, even with a vacuum in the steam space, there is always sufficient differential across the trap to remove the condensate. But the pump must be able to handle the maximum load of condensate, flash steam and air and is likely to be expensive.

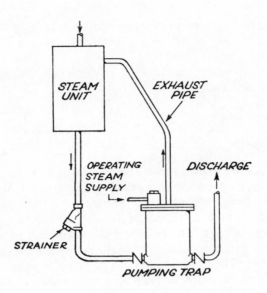

Figure 65

On occasions a pumping trap can be used instead of a normal steam trap on this type of application. We have already said in the previous section that a pumping trap can be used to drain from a vacuum. It can also drain a steam space under pressure although there are limitations to both the vacuum and the pressure on which it will operate. Where the conditions are right, however, it provides a very simple solution to our problem.

It is installed as shown in Figure 65, below the heat exchanger, with the exhaust connected to the top of the steam space. During the filling stroke, when the exhaust valve is open this connection equalizes the pressures in the steam space and the pumping trap body and condensate flows into the latter because of the static head between the two. Care is needed with the details of this installation if it is to work satisfactorily and the makers of the pumping trap should be consulted, if possible.

If the pressure in the steam space can be higher than the maximum at which a pumping trap will work, two separate drain systems can be fitted, together with the necessary valves, so that the operator can change over from one to the other as required. One system consists of the normal steam trap for working under pressure conditions and the other of a pumping trap for the vacuum phase.

Under no circumstances should condensate be lifted directly from a steam trap fitted to this type of application because there will be times when there is insufficient pressure available to overcome the lift.

Always drain the condensate by gravity to a vented receiver and lift it with a pumping trap (Figure 64). Where a pumping trap is used as a drain trap it may be possible to use this also to lift the condensate, but there are limits to the height through which it can be raised and again the makers' advice should be sought.

Steam trap maintenance

Having gone to the trouble of installing steam traps correctly it is, of course, essential that they should receive regular maintenance to keep them in proper working order. Failure to do so may well result in considerable waste of energy due to blowing steam and, in addition, material being processed may be spoiled.

Because working conditions vary so widely it is difficult to be dogmatic about service intervals. It is suggested that all steam traps should be inspected at least annually and even more frequently should operating experience show this to be desirable. Do not forget to clean the strainer screens at the same time.

4 Heat transfer and air

Resistant films

In Chapter 1 we said that the rate at which heat would flow from steam in the steam space of the plant to the material being heated depended on a number of factors. Since the whole purpose of providing a boiler plant to generate steam and a distribution system to carry it to the plant is to use the heat which it contains to process some material as efficiently as possible, the importance of the heat transfer operation becomes clear.

At first sight there is no problem. Steam condenses on one side of the metal wall through which the heat passes to the product on the other side, dropping in temperature on the way because of the resistance of the metal. But Figure 66 shows that it is not like that at all. On the product side, depending on the material being heated, there may be a film of scale or burnt product and a further film of stagnant product. And on the steam side there will probably be another film of rust or scale and there will be a film of condensate and another of air, these last two forming in places a complicated mixture.

Each of these films slows down the flow of heat to a greater or lesser extent and in combination they have a vastly greater effect than the metal wall itself.

We must now see why they are there and what we can do to reduce the harm which they do.

Stagnant product film

This is most readily understood in considering a very viscous product. If tar is being heated in a vessel by a steam coil, the adjacent tar first melts and gets hotter and hotter because it cannot quickly move away by circulation. The melted tar thus forms a resistance to heat flow to the next layer. It is easy to see that some liquids, milk for example, could easily burn on to the metal wall in similar circumstances and form a film of burnt-on product which needs physically to be removed before heat transmission becomes normal again.

Circulation, or some way of engendering movement in the product, is thus seen to be a help to heat transmission. Even a heating coil in a liquor tank is more efficient if it is vertical instead of flat on the bottom. A fine example of this is the heater in a brewing copper.

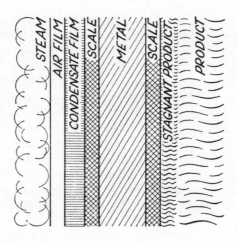

Figure 66

Scale films

As we have seen a film of product or scale can very easily form on the metal surface. Fluff on the heating surface of an air heater battery or textile dryer, scale on a pipe coil heating up hard water and a thin film of clear toffee burnt onto the wall of a steam jacketed toffee pan are examples. In all these cases the accumulating material causes a steady fall-off in performance and regular cleaning is necessary if output is to be kept up.

Next we come to the metal wall, which is such a good conductor of heat compared with the resistant films that a change of material, say from stainless steel to copper with its higher conductivity, is of little practical consequence.

But the side of the metal on which the steam condenses may also have a film of rust or scale which has collected over a long period of time without anybody thinking to have a look and see if it is there. Indeed many process plants are made so that it is very difficult to see inside the steam space, let alone clean it out. The fact that heat transfer surfaces in boilers, where there is a difference of the order of 600 °C between one side and the other, are cleaned regularly, should make those responsible for process plant where the difference is only about 40 °C draw the obvious conclusion.

The condensate film

The next film is one we already know something about, being formed by the water produced as the steam condenses on the metal wall in giving up its Specific enthalpy of evaporation. It is not possible to prevent the condensate film from forming but its harmful effect of reducing heat flow can be kept to a minimum, by ensuring that it is not thicker than it need be.

The first thing is to see the steam reaching the plant is as near dry saturated as possible. Wet steam simply deposits more water on the heat transfer surface.

This question of steam quality has already been discussed in some detail in Chapter 1 with particular reference to the use of Steam Dryers. Further reference to the draining of steam mains, which has an important bearing on steam quality, is made in Chapter 11.

More condensate than necessary will also form if the plant is being asked to do more work than it should. Drying is a very common industrial process which is often carried out in two stages. First of all a great deal of the moisture is removed mechanically by centrifuges, squeeze rolls, suction notches and the like and then the material is finally dried by heat. If the efficiency of the mechanical part of the drying process falls off, a greater load is thrown on the steam heated dryer which condenses more steam in consequence and increases the amount of condensate on the heating surface. Even if the steam dryer can do the extra work, this is an expensive way of getting the material dry and the overall efficiency of the plant suffers.

Excessive condensate on the heating surface is also produced by carrying out the process at too high a temperature. Even if this does not harm the material being heated, heat losses from the plant will be higher than they need be and this, in turn, means that more steam is being condensed than the process really requires. Many heating processes will benefit from the use of automatic temperature regulators which can be set to maintain the temperature which experiment shows to be the lowest at which satisfactory results are obtained.

It is also wasteful to overdry material so that immediately it leaves the dryer it regains moisture from the atmosphere.

If air is used for drying, it is nearly always possible to recirculate it across the wet material several times before it is discharged to waste. Unless this is done, the heat consumption of the dryer will be inefficiently high, as will the condensation rate in the steam space. We will return to this point again in Chapter 8.

Having reduced the formation of condensate to the minimum necessary to carry out the process and assuming that it can flow freely off the heating surface to the drain point, its removal and control is the function of the steam trap.

Chapter 2 has already described the characteristics and types of steam traps, but this is only a small part of the story. They are not gadgets to be stuck on the ends of pipes in the hope that condensate will flow to them and out of them at the appropriate rate. Properly used, steam traps are a means of increasing production from steam heated plant, or, conversely, of saving fuel. Most of this book tries to tell you how and why.

The air film

Finally we come to the air film which is the main subject of this chapter. Air is a particularly poor conductor of heat – which is why it forms the main component of most heat insulation – and its presence on the heat transfer surface can seriously reduce heat flow to the product. In fact the thermal conductivity of air is 0.03 watts per square metre per °C temperature difference per metre thickness (0.03 W/m °C). This should be compared with 0.7 for water, 50 for iron and

380 for copper and shows that a film of air only 0.025 mm thick resists heat flow to the same extent as a wall of copper 320 mm thick. In addition the presence of air in steam will reduce steam temperature, as we shall shortly see.

The main reason for air being in the steam space at all lies in what happens when plant is shut down and steam turned off. The steam left in the steam space condenses and forms a partial vacuum which is then filled by air coming in through steam traps, valve glands and joints. When the time comes to turn steam on again the steam space will be full of air.

In addition, the boiler feed water contains a small amount of air and carbon dioxide in solution, even when it has been efficiently de-aerated, and when the water is boiled these gases are released and carried with the steam into the plant. Here the steam condenses but the gases do not and are deposited onto the heating surface where they will stay unless there is some means of getting rid of them. Although the proportions of non-condensable gases in the incoming steam will be small, if they do not get away freely the build-up will be cumulative. Also, they are unlikely to collect evenly on the heating surface, so that heat transfer, too, will be uneven and the product may be unevenly dried and spoiled. In this chapter we will use the word 'air' to include incondensable gases such as carbon dioxide as well.

Air reduces temperature

We have already said that one effect of mixing air with steam is to lower the temperature. For the reason we must go to Dalton's law of partial pressures which can be stated: 'In a mixture of gases and/or vapours the total pressure of the mixture is made up of the partial pressures exerted by each gas or vapour. The partial pressure exerted by each is the fraction of the total pressure equal to the fraction of the total volume of each.'

The pressure is in absolute units.

For example, the total pressure of a mixture of air and steam is 140 kPa absolute. The mixture is made up of 3 parts of steam and 1 part of air.

The partial pressure of the steam is $\frac{3}{4} \times 140 = 105$ kPa absolute.

The partial pressure of the air is $\frac{1}{4} \times 140 = 35$ kPa absolute.

The temperature of dry saturated steam at 140 kPa absolute is 109 °C. This is what the temperature should be if dry saturated steam alone were filling the space.

But if the space is filled with the mixture of 3 parts steam and 1 part air, the partial pressure of the steam is only 105 kPa absolute. The temperature of steam at this pressure is 101 °C.

The air component of the mixture does not supply any heat so that the temperature of the mixture can be only 101 °C instead of 109 °C which would be registered if there were no air present.

Steam heated plant working with this mixture is, in effect, working at virtually 0 kPa gauge instead of the 38 kPa which appears on the pressure gauge. This effect is particularly serious in those plants, such as sterilizers and canning retorts, which rely on steam at a certain pressure to heat the material being sterilized or cooked to a definite temperature. Any failure to achieve this temperature can have serious consequences.

Practical effect of air in the steam space

Exact theoretical calculation of the savings to be made by the elimination of air from steam spaces is quite impossible because there are so many variable factors.

There is, however, considerable practical evidence that it does lead to increased performance of industrial plant.

To give a few examples – the removal of air from the cylinders of a horizontal textile drying machine reduced the heating-up time from 90 minutes to 10 minutes. The temperature difference between the inlet and exhaust end of the cylinders was reduced from 16 °C to 3 °C.

Air removal from the cylinders of a two-stack sixteen-cylinder vertical textile dryer so improved performance as to save 1 tonne of coal a week.

Air removal from the steam space of a jacketed pan used for jam making reduced the cooking time from 11 minutes to 9 minutes 5 seconds and the steam consumption from 2.66 kg per kg of water evaporated from the jam to 2.00 kg per kg of water evaporated.

Air removal from the steam space of a 455 litre jacketed pan used for soup-making reduced the cooking time from $28\frac{1}{2}$ minutes to 18 minutes and the steam consumption per batch from 81 kg to 73 kg.

Perhaps enough has been written to show the advantages of removing air from steam spaces, and we will now move on and see how to set about it.

Air vents

Certain types of steam trap will remove such air as reaches them with the condensate.

If the shape of the steam space is such that the general direction of steam flow is towards the trap (Figure 67) it is probable that most of the air will get out this way and the percentage of air in the steam will be very low. If, however, the shape of the steam space is such that steam or condensate can get to the trap

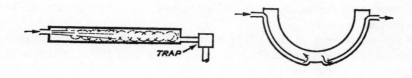

Figure 67   Figure 68

before all the air is discharged (Figure 68) then the steam trap alone cannot sufficiently reduce the percentage of air and additional means of discharging the air must be fitted.

The first and obvious solution to this problem is to fit a hand-operated vent cock on the steam space. The plant operator would have to open this before steam is turned on and to close it when steam escaped. Even in theory this is not too easy because the air is present as an air/steam mixture and looks like live steam, so it is almost impossible for the operator to know just when to close the cock.

It is even more difficult for the operator to know when sufficient air has collected in the steam space, due to incoming steam, to warrant the cock being opened again.

A practical example of this is shown in the working of a laundry calender. Calender beds are sometimes fitted with air vent cocks and it is the practice for these vents to be opened in the morning on starting up, so that the air can be blown out. The vents are shut by guesswork. When this procedure is carried out, it is not uncommon to find that the calender seems to get tired as the day goes on and the work is not being dried so well. This sluggishness is due to the gradual building up of a higher air/steam ratio by the air coming originally from the feedwater.

Now there is one factor which does differentiate an air/steam mixture from the pure steam and that is its temperature. This can be used to provide an air vent which is entirely automatic in operation.

A thermostatic air vent is no different in principle from a thermostatic steam trap. The most convenient type works on the balanced pressure principle, described on pages 44 – 6 and Figure 23. It is important that the temperature difference (t) between the boiling point of water at any pressure and the boiling point of the filling of the thermostatic element at the same pressure should be as small as possible. This temperature difference will settle what the temperature of the air/steam mixture must be before the vent opens and this in turn depends upon the percentage of air present. It must, however, be pointed out that if t is small, p is also small and hence the power available to close the valve against any dirt present on the seat is small. For this reason the majority of air vents are constructed to give satisfactory results on most applications, but special near-to-steam elements are available for such equipment as hospital sterilizers and steaming ovens where complete air removal is vital and the occasional failure to shut off tight against dirt is of no importance.

It must also be remembered that a thermostatic air vent, operating on the balanced pressure principle, cannot be used if there is any danger of waterhammer or superheat reaching the element.

The advantages of air venting are at their greatest in process and heating steam installations, and it is unusual and generally unwise to employ superheat for these purposes. Nevertheless the problem does sometimes arise of venting the air from a superheated steam space or from a steam main where waterhammer does occur. In these cases a bimetallic air vent can be used and this is similar to the bimetallic steam traps described on pages 46–9.

Position of the air vent

In deciding on the number and positions of the air vents needed for a particular machine two main factors must be borne in mind. The first is the importance of getting the air out quickly before it has a chance to mix with the incoming steam. Once the air and steam are mixed together they can only be separated by condensing the steam and depositing the air on the heat transfer surface.

The second point is that, in most cases, the steam coming in will tend to push the air in front of it until it reaches some point or points remote from the inlet, where it will collect. Here it will form a pocket, unless removed, and gradually diffuse back into the steam to form a mixture. The temperature of the heating surface where the air pocket collects will be much lower than that in contact with steam.

It is interesting to note that in most plants the fact that air is heavier than steam does not mean that it falls to the bottom of the steam space. The dynamic effect of the entering steam and the shape of the steam space are the governing factors. There are exceptions to this but these are generally very large steam spaces, such as autoclaves and retorts, where there is a very big volume of air on which the incoming steam has less effect.

One further point is that sometimes, but by no means always, the condensate drain point is also the best point from which to remove the air. If a considerable amount of air has to come out by way of the drain point then either a steam trap that is capable of venting air efficiently must be used, or a separate air vent must be fitted in parallel with it.

We will now show how air venting should be done in practice by examining a number of different cases.

Figure 69

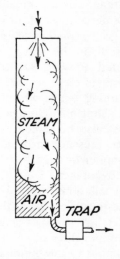

Figure 70

Figures 69 and 70 show two steam spaces identical in shape and size. In Figure 69 steam enters at the bottom while in Figure 70 it comes in at the top. In both cases, of course, the condensate drain point is at the bottom. When steam is turned on to Figure 69 it will push the air ahead of it to the remote point, which is at the top of the steam space and this is where the air vent should be fitted. The trap will have little or no air to deal with.

But in Figure 70 the reverse is the case. The air will be pushed down to the drain point by the steam coming in at the top and we must either fit a trap which has air venting capacity, such as a float trap with inbuilt air vent, or fit a separate air vent in parallel with the trap.

Laundry ironers

The air venting of laundry ironer beds is particularly important, not only because they are required to give a high heat output, but because uneven heating across the width of the bed may cause distortion and damage to the clothing of the rolls and to the material passing through the machine.

Ironer beds vary greatly in design and each should be examined individually to determine the best place for the air vents. Figure 71 shows one example. Here the steam space is divided up by internal partitions and the steam coming in pushes the air across the machine, round the partition through 180 degrees and back to the inlet end again where the drain point is situated. Some of the air will

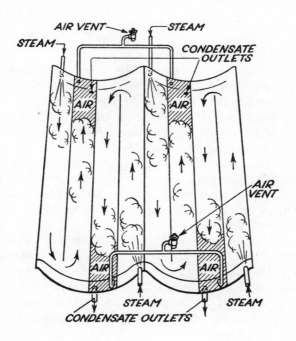

Figure 71

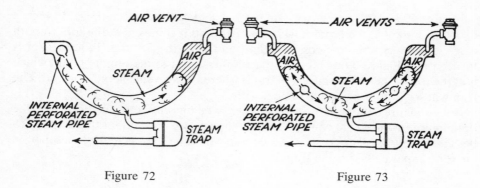

Figure 72   Figure 73

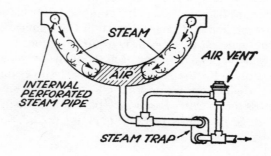

Figure 74

go out through the trap, which is preferably a float type with thermostatic air vent in this case, and the rest will need a separate air vent fitted as shown to vent the air from two sections of the bed at the same time.

Figures 72 to 74 show a cross-section through the bed of an older design of ironer which provides a very good example of how the remote point for air venting varies with the position of the steam inlet.

In Figure 72 steam enters the bed through a perforated pipe running the full width of the machine along one horn. It pushes the air in front of it and some passes out through the drain point so that the trap must be capable of discharging air. The remainder collects in the opposite horn where an air vent should be fitted at each end of the ironer.

Figure 73 shows a different arrangement of steam inlet. Two perforated pipes are now used and they are positioned half-way up towards the horns discharging steam two ways. There are now three remote points, one at either horn and one at the drain point, and air vents must be fitted as shown.

Finally Figure 74 shows yet another variation. A perforated pipe runs across each horn and all the air is pushed down to the drain point. A trap with good air venting characteristics is vital here or a separate air vent must be fitted in parallel.

Jacketed pans

Figure 75 shows where air collects in the steam space of a fixed jacketed pan. The inlet is at the side and the outlet from the bottom. A is the point remote from the steam inlet. Its exact position can often be found in practice by observing the surface of the liquid being heated, activity being markedly less at this point. The fitting of an air vent at A will reduce the boiling time.

Figure 76 shows where air collects in the steam space of a fixed jacketed pan with bottom inlet and outlet. Such designs show a greater tendency to collect air, since little will go out through the drain point. The fitting of an air vent at A, the remote point, to a 455 litre pan reduced the cooking time, as mentioned earlier, by 38 %.

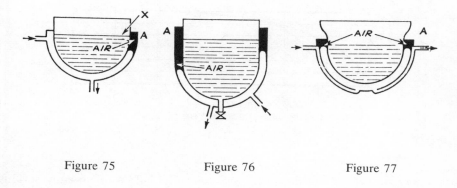

Figure 75   Figure 76   Figure 77

Figure 77 shows the conditions in a tilting jacketed pan fed by steam at the bottom and drained from the bottom. In such pans the air collection is fairly general right round the top of the jacket. In several cases tested air venting at A reduced cooking time by 15–20 %.

The figures given in these examples are actual test figures but they must vary from job to job depending on the material of the pan, the product, the shape of the steam space, the rate of condensation and the temperature head.

Large steam spaces

Certain industries use large retorts or autoclaves in which the material being processed is brought directly into contact with the steam. Examples are rubber autoclaves and food canning and milk sterilizing retorts. Hospitals, too, use autoclaves for sterilizing dressings and various other objects.

In all these processes the material has to be raised to a certain fairly critical temperature and held there for a period, and a common factor in all cases is a large chamber full of air when steam is first turned on.

We have already seen how the temperature of an air/steam mixture is lower than that of pure steam at the same pressure, so unless the chamber is

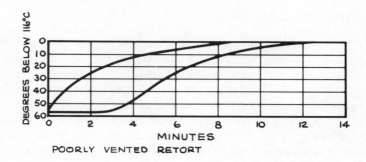

Figure 78

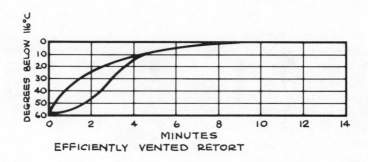

Figure 79

thoroughly purged of air the process is likely to fail, with possibly serious consequences. Raising the pressure is no solution because the air will not be evenly distributed and heat treatment will not be uniform.

Tests on a badly vented milk sterilizing retort showed that not only was heating up slow but the bottles in the bottom of the retort never reached sterilizing temperature. Proper air venting cut the heating up time from 40 minutes to 16½ minutes and all the milk was properly sterilized.

Figure 78 shows the effect of air on the heating up of a vertical canning retort. Although the outside cans had reached the required temperature of 116 °C after 8 minutes, the inside ones were still 11 °C below this temperature and took a further 6 minutes to catch up. Figure 79 shows the effect of proper air venting which brought the inside cans to the same temperature as the outside cans in just over 4 minutes.

Air venting of these large chambers has to take into account the large volume of air on start-up, the need for removing it quickly to minimize mixing with the steam, the position and method of injecting the steam and any obstruction to flow caused by the material in the retort. Since venting is most effective if it takes place so rapidly that pressure is unable to build up in the retort during the venting period, this factor together with the large amount of air points to the use of air vents with a total capacity that is much higher than is needed on steam spaces where heat transfer is indirectly through a heating surface.

The position of the steam inlet and the amount of obstruction caused by the contents of the retort are, to some extent, connected. Some obstruction by the contents is usually unavoidable, but should be kept to a minimum to reduce the formation of air pockets which will seriously reduce temperature. It is particularly important that any flooring used in the retort should be of the open grid type to allow free flow of air, steam and condensate.

In most retorts it is traditional for steam to be injected at the bottom and any air vents provided are at the top. But we have already said that in large spaces the fact that air is denser than steam becomes significant. Logically, therefore, the better arrangement would seem to be to inject the steam at the top and vent the air from the bottom. In this way the intermixing of steam with air is likely to be less. In practice, if the contents of the chambers seriously obstruct steam flow, such as happens with cans packed into a canning retort, top or bottom steam entry give comparable results because of the very real difficulty of moving pockets of air trapped between the cans.

Theory would also suggest that the steam should be injected into the chamber at low velocity through a number of inlets spread evenly over the whole area of the chamber. This is also correct in practice, unless the contents seriously obstruct the steam flow when it has been proved better to inject the steam with considerable velocity into the likely pockets of stagnant air.

Balanced pressure thermostatic air vents can be used for venting retorts provided that they can be fitted in sufficient numbers to deal with the volume of air but it should be realized that they close at a temperature below that of saturated steam. This means that some air will remain in the chamber unless it has been possible to reduce mixing of the air and steam to the minimum and in some cases this will not be acceptable. In these cases a temperature regulator can

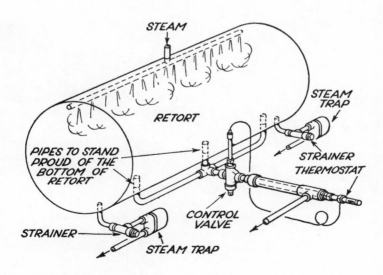

Figure 80

be used and this can be set to close off at a specified temperature regardless of pressure. Since a temperature regulator allows the use of a really large valve the air can be vented rapidly without pressure building up in the chamber. At the same time the thermostat can be set to keep the valve open until really air-free steam reaches it.

Figure 80 shows the arrangement.

These examples can do no more than show the general principles underlying the siting of air vents; practical consideration must modify the ultimate choice of position. Just as a steam trap can discharge only the condensate which reaches it, so air vents are quite useless if they are fitted in the wrong place. Air removal is so important that it is worth a little thought to see how the practical difficulties of fitting an air vent can be overcome and the general theory applied.

Fortunately, manufacturers of process steam equipment are realising the effect which air venting can have on the output of the plant which they supply and an increasing number of them are providing means for proper air removal.

When discussing various types of steam heated equipment in the chapters which follow we shall indicate the best way of removing air from them.

5 Low potential heat

Engineers have for generations been concerned with the raising of steam. It has also been their job to design, erect and run the power engines in which some of this steam is used. It is only comparatively recently that they have been allowed to have any hand in the running of the process plant in which most of their steam is used and then only in the more enlightened firms. Otherwise this remains the job of the production man, or the works manager, or the chemist, who are seldom steam experts. Not only are all steams alike to them, but the availability of steam is something which they accept as a right – like water at the tap. The cost of steam – even if they know what it is – is generally only a small percentage of the total cost of production. Apart therefore from plant maintenance, the boiler house, steam distribution and condensate return systems and the power plant, if there is one, are the engineer's job. Here the cost of steam raising and the cost of power is the be-all and end-all.

It follows naturally that generations of engineers have concentrated their energies on efficient steam raising and power generation and have designed the steam raising plant to suit their own efficiencies. Generations of production men have turned on steam valves and have been content if the heat came out fast enough to complete their process in the time to which they were accustomed.

It was because of this unfortunate division of interest that the efficiency of industrial steam usage lagged far behind the efficiency of industrial steam raising and it is only in the last thirty years or so that the latter has started to catch up. The result is that in many cases the process steam user is left with unsuspected supplies of heat of considerable value either to himself or the boiler plant; the steam raiser and the power steam user have similar supplies of heat of value to the process user.

Some of these available heat supplies are a function of steam trapping, but we make no excuse for briefly mentioning others, which may appear to be outside the scope of this book, because of the great contribution which they can make to overall steam plant efficiency.

Flash steam recovery

The value of hot condensate as boiler feed is so generally known that there would be no need to mention it again were it not for the fact that there are still hundreds of litres of valuable heat-carrying water being put down the drains of industrial plants every hour.

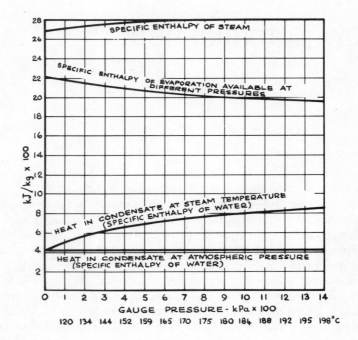

Figure 81

Assuming, however, that this particular point is realized, it is general practice for condensate to be discharged through steam traps to a common main from which it flows to the boiler feed tank either by gravity, or by steam pressure through the traps, or to a tank or sump and thence by pumping. The feed pump then puts it back into the boiler.

The common condensate main is usually at approximately atmospheric pressure, but there is steam pressure at the inlet to the trap and the condensate is often at steam temperature, or very little below.

Figure 81 shows the Specific enthalpy of steam, evaporation and water under different pressure conditions. For example, at 800 kPa gauge pressure, the Specific enthalpy of water in 1 kg of condensate at the inlet side to the trap may be the full 743 kJ. The heat in condensate at the outlet side can be only 419 kJ. It has been mentioned before that the remaining heat (324 kJ in this case) will cause some re-evaporation of the water, and flash steam will be formed and pass into the condensate main with the condensate.

Whether or not this flash steam should be left in the main can only be decided in the light of the particular circumstances. If it is allowed to go back to the feed tank, which should be lagged, and the condensate main is also lagged, as it should be, it may not all be condensed in the feed water, in which case there will be a plume of steam escaping from the feed tank vent. This will almost certainly apply in those cases where a high proportion of the condensate is returned to the boiler and the amount of cold make-up water is small.

Even if all the flash is condensed, the resulting feed-water temperature may be so high that the pumps may not be able to handle it, although the provision of a good static head over the pump suction can often help this situation.

When returning flash along the condensate main it is important to make sure that the latter has been sized correctly, otherwise a back pressure will be imposed on the traps draining the plant, which may prevent the free removal of condensate. Even with a well lagged condensate main, heat will be lost in getting the flash steam back to the boiler house, so all these considerations lead to the general conclusion that it is much better to use the flash close to the point where it is being generated if this is at all possible.

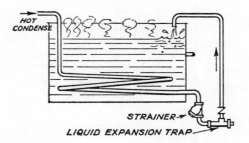

Figure 82

On some plants it is possible to use the Specific enthalpy of water in the condensate before it is discharged. Figure 82 shows a simple example. A coil is used to heat up liquid in a tank to a temperature below boiling point. A liquid expansion trap is fitted on the outlet. Condensate from the trap may be returned to the liquid if its nature allows. Otherwise condensate from the trap is put into the common main at a temperature below 100 °C.

When steam is turned on, air is first discharged. Then cold condensate follows with a free passage. Since condensate held up before the trap has to cool below 100 °C before discharge, it must give up some of its Specific enthalpy of water to the surrounding liquid. The hotter the liquid the longer the hold up, and the capacity of the coil must allow for this. But the point is that the Specific enthalpy of water is being put to the best possible use. A trap of this type so installed will in fact act as an approximate temperature control, by waterlogging some of the coil and reducing the rate of heat transfer as the temperature of the liquid rises and by exposing more steam surface as the temperature of the liquid drops.

Where such controlled waterlogging is not permissible condensate must be discharged at a higher temperature and flash steam is formed.

Figure 83 shows the weight of flash steam formed when one kilogram of condensate at steam temperature and at pressures up to 1500 kPa is discharged to various lower pressures.

Figure 84 shows a simple way of using this steam heat. A heater battery provides air at 150 °C for a drying process using steam at 825 kPa at a rate of

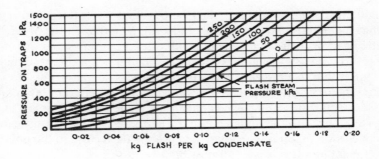

Figure 83

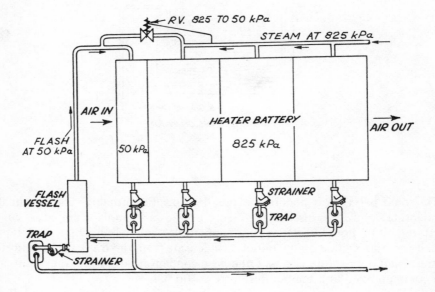

Figure 84

0.3 kg/s. We will assume that if the flash steam was returned to the feed tank with the condensate, the feed water will be too hot to handle, so it will be better to use the flash close to the dryer. This can be done quite simply if the first section of the battery is run on low pressure steam at 50 kPa. The amount of flash available at 50 kPa from the condensate discharged by the traps on the remainder of the battery is 0.044 kg/s. Any further steam required can be supplied through a pilot-operated reducing valve which will maintain a steady pressure in the first section of the battery despite any variation in the amount of flash steam available.

The result in this particular case is a saving in live steam of 14.5 % and in addition, the feed tank problem is also solved. Of course, this is only possible if the battery has sufficient heating surface to allow the steam pressure in the first section to be reduced without loss of output. Otherwise extra surface would have to be provided but should not normally present much of a problem.

There is very often considerable scope for recovering flash steam in a laundry from the calenders, tumblers and presses, using it to preheat the hot water and so saving live steam. The flash steam can be passed through the tube bundle of a calorifier with the water in the shell. Sometimes it is possible to use an old calorifier which will no longer stand the full steam pressure but is perfectly capable of working on low pressure flash steam. A system of this sort will often pay for itself in a surprisingly short space of time because of the very high cost of fuel.

A possible outlet for flash steam utilization is the heating system, although this has the disadvantage of being out of use in the summer months and for this reason should only be considered if there is no other use for the flash. But where the heating system has been designed to work at high pressure, thought should be given to using the flash steam in part of the system at low pressure, even if some extra heating surface has to be provided to compensate for the reduction in surface temperature. But heating surface is one of the best of all investments. It must be paid for only once; but the fuel saving goes on for ever.

As an example, consider a system of overhead pipe coils of the kind used in the textile industry for many years and still in use in a number of mills. These are now usually fed with steam at pressures between 550 and 850 kPa – let us take 700 kPa and assume that the system uses 0.25 kg/s of steam.

The arrangement of piping is generally such that waterhammer is more than probable and so mechanical traps have been chosen to drain the system. These pass condensate at steam temperature. From Figure 83 we see that 1 kg of condensate being reduced from 700 kPa to 70 kPa produces just over 0.12 kg of flash steam, so our pipe system produces 0.03 kg of flash per second at 70 kPa pressure.

The total heat requirements of the system must have been 0.25 × 2048 kW (2048 kJ/kg being the Specific enthalpy of evaporation at 700 kPa) = 512 kW. If we now feed live steam to only 90 % of the system and pass the condensate from that section, through steam traps, to a flash vessel at 70 kPa we have the following state of affairs:

Heat in live steam (90 % of 0.25 kg/s at 700 kPa) = 0.225 × 2048 = 461 kW
Flash steam from 0.225 kg/s at 0.12 kg/kg = 0.027 kg/s at 70 kPa
Heat in flash steam = 0.027 × 2215
$\qquad\qquad\qquad\quad$ = 60 kW
So heat available $\quad$ = 461 + 60
$\qquad\qquad\qquad\quad$ = 521 kW

This means that we have reduced the steam consumption of the heating system by 10 % and still have just the same amount of heat available. At the same time we have solved the problem of disposing of the flash steam. But don't forget the point already made about the need to increase the amount of heating surface.

Flash condensing

A rather special flash steam problem arises in such places as hospitals, university buildings and the like where steam is generated at 550 to 700 kPa in a central boilerhouse and distributed around the site to calorifiers producing hot water for both heating and domestic purposes.

Condensate from the calorifiers has usually to be lifted to high level for return to the boilerhouse and pumps must be used because of the low pressures at the traps, resulting from thermostatic control (see page 99). Because there is no other use for it, flash steam will be lost to atmosphere out of the pump receiver vents. Not only is good heat being lost but these plumes of steam are unsightly and may cause damage to the fabric of the building.

The way in which this flash steam is dealt with depends on whether we are considering a heating or hot water storage calorifier. In the case of a heating calorifier, the best method is to pass the flash through a heat exchanger where it will be condensed in preheating the return water from the heating system (Figure 85).

Both the condensate and flash steam from the calorifier go to a flash steam condenser where the flash is condensed by the return heating water. This flash condenser also acts as a receiver for the condensate pump, so serving a double purpose.

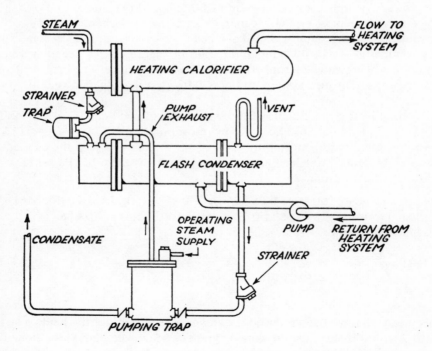

Figure 85

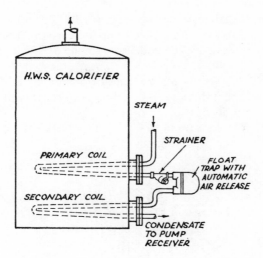

Figure 86

The condensate and flash steam from a hot water storage calorifier are passed through a secondary coil positioned near the bottom (Figure 86) where the cold water feed comes in. When hot water has been drawn off and replaced by cold the flash steam in the secondary coil gives up its heat to the water and is condensed while helping the calorifier to return to storage temperature.

The beauty of both these methods is that there is always water available at a low enough temperature to condense all the flash steam.

Lowering steam pressures

In the calculation on flash steam, perhaps one important fact was not noticed. Steam at 700 kPa gauge has a Specific enthalpy of evaporation of 2048 kJ/kg while steam at 70 kPa has 2215 – 8 % more. If, for some reason, it is not possible to use a flash steam recovery system, it is worth while to consider the advantage of using steam at the lowest possible pressure.

For example, take the case of a mill heating system of the type already discussed. When first put in these used to run at pressures of the order of 1100 kPa because steam was generated at this high pressure for the mill engine. Steam at 1100 kPa has a Specific enthalpy of evaporation of 1986 kJ/kg and if a system of this type had been originally designed to work at 70 kPa throughout it would have used only $88\frac{1}{2}$ % of the steam. It is true that the first cost would have been considerably more, because of the increased heating surfaces required, but over its life the system would have shown a handsome profit.

After a system has been installed it is no easy matter to alter it. The flash steam method is perhaps more easily adopted than the general working on a lower pressure, and when an extension is contemplated careful thought should be given to the availability of flash steam from the existing plant.

When a new system is being designed the cheap running at low pressures should carefully be weighed against the initial cost. For example, an increase of

25 % in the surface of a heating system working at 550 kPa will make it possible to work at a pressure of 240 kPa and save 4 %; an increase of 75 % in the heating surface will allow a pressure of 35 kPa and give a saving of 7 % in the fuel bill for ever.

The heating surfaces of process plant are not often capable of extension. It would seem in such cases that there is no possibility of lowering the pressure and so saving fuel. This is not always so.

In Chapter 4 (page 74) we saw how the various resistant films govern the rate of heat transfer through a heating surface.

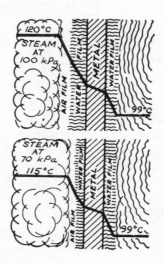

Figure 87

Figure 87 shows diagrammatically the flow of heat from a steam space to a liquid being heated. The final temperature must be 99 °C. The steam temperature must be sufficiently above this for heat to flow through the various films and obstructions between. If the resistance of any of these films can be decreased the steam pressure can be reduced. In the diagram, by reducing the air and water films on the steam side by one half, the steam pressure necessary can be cut from 100 to 70 kPa. So correct steam trapping and air venting not only enable process plant to give its best output but also allow it to operate most efficiently at the lowest possible pressure.

Atmospheric steam

In all evaporating processes steam is given off from the liquid being heated. Sometimes the steam is at atmospheric pressure – for example, in jam making; sometimes it is below atmospheric pressure – for example, in multiple effect evaporators.

In open top boiling processes the steam and the heat which it contains is almost invariably wasted and can, indeed, prove a real nuisance. Where the process is suitable it can be greatly reduced by covering the surface of the boiling liquid with small plastic balls and this is often done in the case of plating vats. Otherwise the vapour must be got rid of as quickly as possible and very often collecting hoods are placed over the pans and vats and the vapour is pulled away. Yet such vapour contains 2676 kJ in each kilogram and is indeed richer in Specific enthalpy of evaporation than the live steam from the boiler.

Consider the case of a jam manufacturer making 90 kg batches of jam in a battery of 6 pans. It is probable that there are about 13 kg of water evaporated from each pan. That means 78 kg of steam generated per battery in perhaps 5 minutes. If the steam were to be collected under a hood – just as at present – but condensed with a circulated water spray instead of being wasted, it would go a long way towards providing hot water for his works. It would be necessary to have live steam available through a calorifier to make up while the pans were not working. But the point is that the large potential heat supply from the pan vapour would not be wasted.

In America some work has been done in compressing low pressure steam taken from the mains of a district heating system at 240 kPa. Where this steam pressure has been too low for plant requirements it has been boosted up to pressures around 550 to 700 kPa. Modified air compressors have been used to do the work. The capital cost of the plant has been rather less than that of a separate boiler plant to do the same work, and operating and fixed charges have been about 18 % less.

Such a system is obviously most worth consideration if the steam supply is at so low a pressure that it cannot be used at all as steam in its existing form and if there is no demand for the hot water which can be derived from it by a simple contact spray method. Some power must be used in the compression process, but if the steam is genuine waste steam it is obvious that the cost of power is small compared with the value of the heat which is saved.

Another way of getting the same result is by feeding the low pressure waste steam to an injector and boosting it there by a higher pressure live steam to give steam at a usable mixed pressure from the outlet. The compressor method is liable to give superheated steam at the outlet, which may or may not be a disadvantage. The injector method will give saturated steam, and the plant is much simpler, but the final pressure obtainable is not likely to be high.

One difficulty in using the atmospheric steam produced in these batch processes is the lack of continuity in the supply. Some additional source of make-up must be provided as well as reliable pressure or temperature control. These problems are far from being insoluble and the great economy to be effected by putting to good use this otherwise waste heat should never be forgotten.

A further source of heat in atmospheric steam is the exhaust from boiler feed pumps where these are steam driven. And quite apart from any heat in the exhaust steam there is the nuisance caused when these pumps discharge to atmosphere.

The simplest method of recovery is to pass the exhaust through a coil in the feed tank with the result that every 6 °C rise in feed water temperature means a saving of about 1% of the fuel used.

In some cases the feed water is already as hot as the feed pump can stand without cavitation occurring at the pump suction. In these cases a heat exchanger (feed water heater) can be fitted in the feed line between pump and boiler and the pump exhaust passed through it.

Boiler blowdown

Boiler blowdown not only carries away good heat in the water but flash steam is also formed due to the reduction in pressure.

Where the blowdown is intermittent it is difficult to recover this waste heat effectively but the situation is quite different when continuous blowdown is practised since up to as much as 10 % of the boiler evaporation may be discharged.

The simplest form of heat recovery is to condense the flash steam either by water spray or heat exchanger, using the cold make-up water, and to discharge the blowdown water with its heavy concentration of solids, to waste. The flash can, of course, be used as low pressure steam if desired.

But since the blowdown water contains a lot of useful heat as well as sludge some attempt should be made to recover as much of this heat as possible. Bearing in mind that every litre of water blown down from the boiler has to be replaced by cold feed, all that is needed is to pass the hot blowdown through a heat exchanger so that it can transfer its heat to the cold feed water. A further advantage of doing this is that the blowdown will be cooled sufficiently for it to be discharged to waste without causing a nuisance.

Figure 88 shows a typical heat recovery system and includes the extraction of heat from the feed pump exhaust, which has already been described.

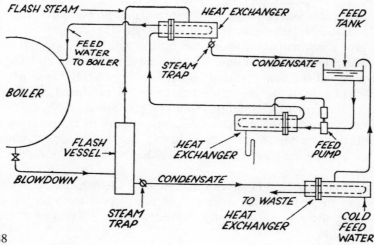

Figure 88

Condenser cooling water

When a power heat circuit was discussed in Chapter 1 (page 28), the point was made that steam should be taken from the power plant at some stage in the expansion and thus made available for process work at a suitable pressure. By this means by far the most efficient use is made of the steam.

It often happens that a condensing turbine has been installed, because only the power angle has been considered, and the process heat requirements have been overlooked. In such plants there is a large heat supply available in the cooling water of a surface condenser. The temperature of this water, at perhaps 35 to 38 °C, may not be sufficient as it comes from the condenser, but it can easily be raised that little bit extra by a calorifier. The resulting hot water must surely have many uses in a plant which is large enough to have such a type of power unit. In the larger power plants the condenser cooling water carries enough heat to supply a small district heating system.

Diesel engine waste heat

Where diesel engines are used to generate power both the cooling water and the exhaust gases contain considerable amounts of heat which often go to waste. Heat exchangers and waste heat boilers can be installed to recover this heat either in the form of hot water or steam and should always be considered unless the engines are purely for stand-by purposes where the capital cost of the equipment would not be justified.

6 Heating, kitchen and hospital equipment

Hot water supply

Heating calorifiers

Steam is often used in non-storage calorifiers to produce hot water for space heating. Except on small installations, it is normal practice to maintain the water leaving the calorifier at a fixed temperature by throttling the steam supply through a valve, which is automatically operated by a temperature-sensitive bulb in the water. The temperature of the heating system is then varied by some form of control valve on the water circuit. On small systems it is possible to vary the water temperature by a valve on the steam supply, operated by a thermostat bulb outside the building, responding to changes in outside air temperature. To prevent the calorifier from boiling should the air temperature fall to a very low figure, a second bulb is normally placed in the water to override the outside bulb and close the valve.

In either case the steam requirements will vary from a maximum, either when the system is started up from cold or when the outside temperature is very low calling for maximum heat output from the system, to very nearly nothing when the outside temperature is high. The pressure in the steam space will also vary very considerably from the maximum rated pressure down to practically nothing. Indeed it is quite common for a vacuum to form in the heating coils when the control valve is practically shut at times of minimum heat demand.

The steam trap must, therefore, be able to work efficiently over a wide range of loads and pressures and this indicates the use of the float type with an automatic air release to clear the air from the battery (Figure 89).

The draining of horizontal calorifiers is straight-forward and this is also true of those vertical units with a single-pass battery, where steam enters at the top and condensate is drained away from the bottom. But some vertical calorifiers are two-pass units in which steam enters at the bottom and the tubes take the form of an inverted U (Figure 90). With this arrangement nearly half of the condensate will drain back into the inlet section of the header and some makers provide a small drain hole through the wall of the midfeather separating the inlet and outlet headers so that this condensate can pass through to the steam trap.

Sometimes this hole can act as a by-pass, allowing steam through to the outlet header and trapping air in the top of the U so that the output of the calorifier is reduced. The best practice is to do away with this hole and trap each section of the header individually as in Figure 90.

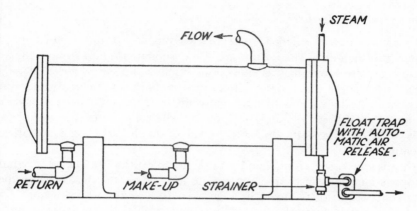

Figure 89

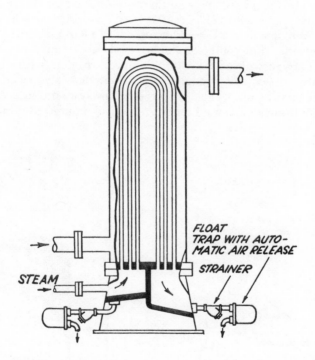

Figure 90

In all cases the traps should be fitted close to the job to avoid steam locking and pipe strainers are always desirable.

Because the pressure at the trap can fall to such a low value it is bad practice to try and lift the condensate directly. This leads to waterlogging of the coils and then, when the control valve opens, steam rushes in and produces violent waterhammer. It is much better to drain the condensate by gravity to a receiver and use an automatic pump to lift it into the overhead return (see page 69). If a direct lift is attempted then a robust inverted bucket trap should be used with an automatic air vent in parallel with it.

Hot water service calorifiers

Hot water service calorifiers can be of two types – storage calorifiers and instantaneous heaters. The latter are very similar to non-storage heating calorifiers and are sometimes used in conjunction with a hot water storage tank and at others supply hot water direct to the user. In all cases the water temperature is usually controlled automatically by a regulator, which may have either an 'ON–OFF' or a modulating action. Where there are likely to be long periods with no draw-off, the control valve should shut tight to prevent overheating.

The traps must, therefore, handle peak loads efficiently when the control valve opens and must discharge condensate as soon as it forms, because these heaters condense a lot of steam in a small space and any waterlogging of the steam space – even temporarily – is most undesirable. Steam locking and air binding should be prevented and a strainer fitted. The best choice is a float type with automatic air release (Figure 91). An inverted bucket trap with an automatic air vent in a by-pass should be used if condensate is lifted directly from the trap. But this direct lift should be avoided because of the inevitable waterhammer. Even with an 'ON–OFF' control, residual steam in the battery when the valve closes will condense and when the valve opens the sudden increase in steam pressure will act on this condensate to produce waterhammer. So once again, drain to a vented receiver and use a pump to do the lifting.

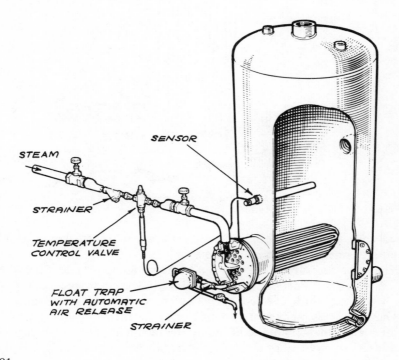

Figure 91

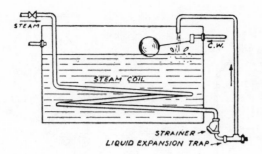

Figure 92

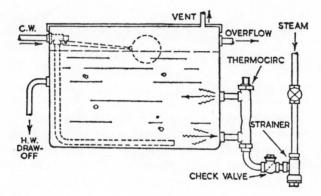

Figure 93

Hot water tanks

Open coil heated tanks are often used to provide hot water for washing or process use in factories.

Figure 92 shows a method of trapping and air venting these which gives maximum economy. The trap is of the liquid expansion type, which is adjustable and can be set to keep the water from boiling excessively by partially waterlogging the coil when the draw off is light.

Figure 93 shows a simple method of temperature controlled direct injection for heating the water. The liquid expansion element in the Thermocirc is very similar to that of the steam trap, but it is actually surrounded by the water being heated and so picks up temperature changes more readily.

Air in hot water

Figures 94 and 95 show two methods of removing the air which collects in the high places of hot water systems. The operation of both types is obvious. When no air is present, hot water lifts the float and closes the outlet valve. As air

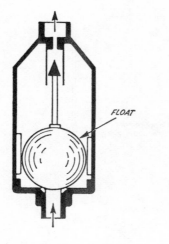

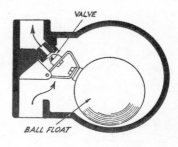

Figure 94   Figure 95

collects it displaces the water causing the float to fall and open the valve. Synthetic rubber valves are often used to ensure a tight shut-off. It is also possible to obtain air eliminators which incorporate a stop valve on the inlet side so that the unit can be dismantled for maintenance without the system having to be drained.

Steam heating

Pipe heating

A pipe heating system in which the pipes are properly laid out with an adequate fall in the direction of flow and steam traps and air vents correctly sited is a simple and efficient means of space heating. An old fashioned system where no attention has been paid to these elementary matters can be an abomination.

Figure 96 shows such a system. There are 375 m of continuous 50 mm (2″) pipe arranged overhead to heat a space. It is impossible to allow a proper fall because of head room which must be at least 3.5 m and there is only 4 m at maximum. So that in the full length of 375 m there is only a fall of 0.5 m (4 mm in 3 m). Condensate as it forms must be pushed all the way round to one large trap on the floor in the corner. Waterhammer is certain to be serious because of dips which have been made and because of the quite inadequate fall. The steam pressure is 1100 kPa.

This description is not a heating engineer's nightmare, but a once common method of heating in textile mills. The steam trap is probably an open bucket type with a hand air release. Heating up of such a system takes hours. All the air has to be driven out of the air cock on the trap, all the condensate must be chased round the system.

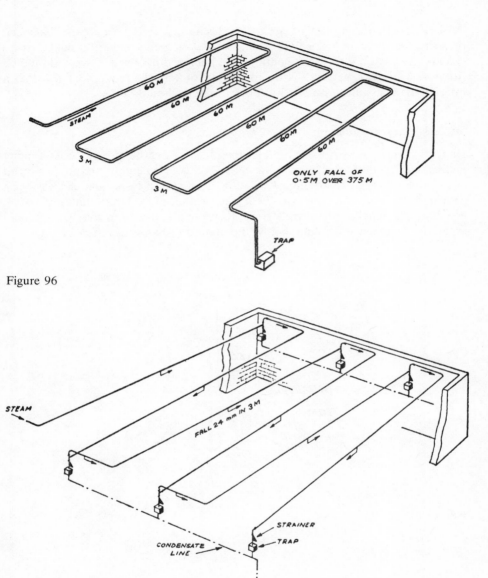

Figure 96

Figure 97

Figure 97 shows the same heating system modernized. Each length of end-to-end piping has been given the full permissible fall of 0.5 m in 63 m (24 mm in 3 m). No condensate has to be taken more than 63 m. There are six small steam traps to vent air quickly. There are no waterlogged pipes and no waterhammer. The same heating effect will be obtained from a much lower steam pressure, which in itself will save fuel. Heat will get round the system in a matter of minutes.

Because of the amount of air to be discharged it is best to use balanced pressure thermostatic traps with stainless steel elements. Inverted bucket traps can also be used but to speed heating up a balanced pressure air vent should be fitted in a by-pass. If there is no likelihood of waterhammer float traps with internal air vents are a possibility. Pipe strainers should be used.

Space heating by radiation

Radiant panels and strips have taken the place of overhead pipe coils in many factories for a number of reasons. Comfortable working conditions are produced even though the air temperature is below normal and local heat can easily be provided without the need to heat the whole of a large building. Also, installation is much more flexible since, for example, in a shop with an overhead crane the panels can be slung below the crane rails without difficulty.

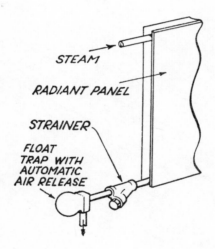

Figure 98

Output depends on high surface temperatures and complete condensate and air removal is essential. For best results trap each panel or strip individually using a float trap with automatic air vent, thermodynamic or inverted bucket traps (Figure 98). It is often satisfactory to group two panels to one trap. Where thermodynamic traps are used arrange the outlet piping so that each trap has a free discharge, otherwise if two traps fitted close to each other discharge at the same time the local back pressure may rise too high and prevent the traps from closing.

If long lengths of radiant strip are temperature controlled by a modulating regulator, the reduction in pressure may prevent proper condensate removal and result in uneven heat distribution.

Steam radiators

The standard multi-column cast iron radiator is most commonly fitted with a small and inexpensive trap of the balanced pressure type. If the steam enters at the top and condensate is discharged from the bottom, as shown in Figure 99, the position of the trap is also the best position for air venting, so that there is no tendency for air to collect in the radiator. If, however, the steam inlet is at the bottom, air discharge will not be so satisfactory and the top of the radiator at the side away from the steam inlet will be cooler than it should be, because of air which does not get down to the trap. If the trap has a thermostatic element which operates below steam temperature, and if the trap is fitted direct on the radiator outlet, there will be some hold up of condensate in the radiator. Since this means that some of the Specific enthalpy of water is being used to good purpose the practice is sound.

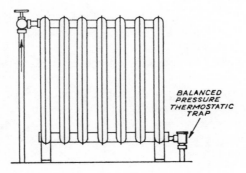

BALANCED
PRESSURE
THERMOSTATIC
TRAP

Figure 99

It is unusual to find strainers fitted before traps on radiators, the theory being that the radiator itself is one big pocket. This is well enough, provided that the system is blown through with steam before it is started up for the winter. The thermostatic elements should be removed while this is done to allow a clear passage for dirt. Any pieces that are too large to pass through the trap orifice can be picked out when the elements are put back.

The convection type of radiator shown in Figure 100 presents quite a different trapping problem. Whereas the steam space of the standard radiator is large compared with the heating surface, the position in the convection radiator is reversed. The steam space is so small that no waterlogging can be tolerated. The balanced pressure thermostatic trap has a great appeal for this work because of its size and price. For maximum heat output it should be fitted about 1 m away from the outlet unless there is some sort of header, as in Figure 100, in which condensate can collect. A small float trap can also be used.

Forced draught convectors have a fan to blow air across the heating surface and are just another form of unit heater (see below). They should be drained with a small float trap.

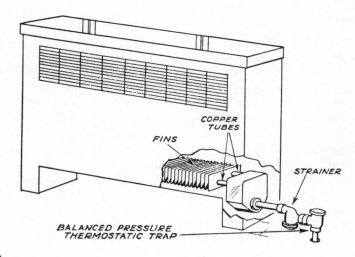

Figure 100

There is more need for strainers on convector radiators because there is no collecting space for dirt.

Radiators are sometimes group-trapped to one larger trap. The practice is not a good one and causes uneven heating, steam locking and sometimes air binding (depending on the type of trap). There is not even a saving in outlay, because, to get the same heating effect, group-trapped radiators will need to be larger than individually trapped ones.

Unit heaters

Unit heaters are no different from radiators of the convection type except that air is blowing through them. They give a particularly heavy rate of condensation from a small steam space. If any water is allowed to lie in the bottom of the unit it will be rapidly cooled by the air draught and will cause a cold blow from the bottom part of the heater. It is not uncommon to find a unit heater blowing hot and cold alternately. The effect is very unpleasant to anybody who has to work in the air stream. The cause is invariably bad steam trapping – not bad steam traps, but either a bad choice of traps or a bad installation.

Because unit heaters are usually suspended, the trap must be up in the air and should be light enough to be carried on the pipework.

There are considerable, and sudden, load variations in a unit heater – particularly if it is thermostatically controlled by the automatic cutting out of the fan motor. The trap should therefore be equally efficient on either light or heavy load.

Since no waterlogging can be tolerated, the trap should discharge condensate at steam temperature and continuously.

The steam space of the unit heater is so small and condensation so rapid that a high percentage of air can quickly be built up unless the air can be discharged. In addition all the air in the pipe feeding the heater must pass through it on starting up and this too must be discharged. The trap must therefore be able to vent air automatically and rapidly.

There is only one steam trap that answers to this specification – that is the float type with thermostatic air release. It is the best recommendation for the job. When condensate has to be lifted after the heater, the trap should be at the bottom of the lift. Figure 101 shows the layout.

Before this small float trap was available it was customary to use balanced pressure thermostatic traps or inverted bucket traps as alternatives to the larger float type because of price considerations. It is true that balanced pressure thermostatic traps will handle load and pressure fluctuations quite satisfactorily and they are ideal for air venting, but whether fitted with near-to-steam element or not they don't discharge condensate continuously, and details of installation have to be carried out very exactly. Unless this is done there is a danger of the traps causing the unit heaters to blow hot and cold.

Because such meticulous care in installation is seldom forthcoming they cannot be considered so practical an alternative as the small float trap.

Inverted bucket traps, too, are often put forward as an alternative. They are light enough for the work and they discharge condensate at steam temperature. But the inverted bucket trap is at its best when load and pressure conditions are steady, and they are apt to be wasteful when working on a light load. Moreover, when air must be discharged quickly on starting up, as is so important on unit heater installations, the inverted bucket trap is not a happy choice. Furthermore, it discharges condensate intermittently and there are many installations where in practice inverted bucket traps are causing the unit heaters to blow hot and cold.

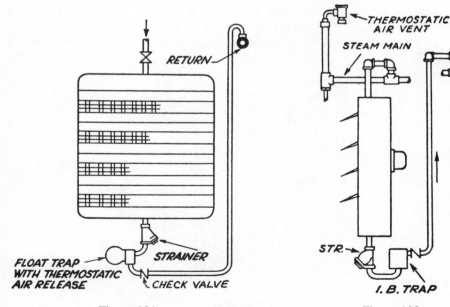

Figure 101   Figure 102

If on existing installations of unit heaters with inverted bucket traps the system takes a long time to heat up, it is often a great help to fit an air vent on the supply main, as shown in Figure 102.

Strainers should be used on these installations whatever the trap chosen. If the heater has small steam tubes it is worth considering fitting the strainer on the heater inlet to prevent large pieces of scale putting a whole tube out of operation.

Heater batteries

Heater batteries are large unit heaters used on air conditioning plant and process dryers and in general the same considerations apply. The trap must keep the battery free from condensate regardless of load and pressure fluctuations, and air removal is vital although the drain connection may no longer be the only natural vent point.

Consider first the question of air venting. If the battery consists of a number of vertical tubes between horizontal headers, the drain point from the bottom header is generally the natural vent point. The steam trap must, therefore, be capable of handling the air rapidly or it should have a separate air vent fitted in parallel. In some cases it may be an advantage to vent the end of the top header furthest from the steam inlet (Figure 103).

In some batteries the tubes run horizontally between headers which can be either horizontal or vertical. If the headers are horizontal, the drain point is likely to be the natural vent point as well, but with vertical headers an air vent should be fitted to the top of the outlet header. With either type provision must be made at the trap for removing air as well.

Because of the variation of load and pressure possible with a heater battery and the importance of keeping the steam space free from condensate at all times, a float trap with thermostatic air release is the best choice. But sometimes heater

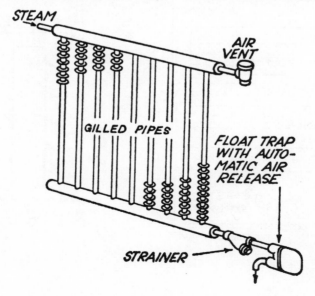

Figure 103

batteries are mounted at floor level and the outlet connections may be very close to the floor so making the fitting of a float trap difficult. In these cases inverted bucket or thermodynamic traps may have to be used but these may need air vents fitted in parallel with them to ensure proper air removal from the battery.

In all cases proper draining and air venting of the steam supply is important to give the heater battery the best chance of producing the required output.

Correct sizing of a heater battery for the work it has to do is important, otherwise there may be problems in getting rid of the condensate. For instance, if a battery is sized to handle an occasional heavy load, but is throttled down most of the time, the pressure in the steam space is likely to be very low indeed and there may even be a vacuum. Under these conditions the lower part of the battery may be waterlogged leading to uneven air temperatures, corrosion of the tubes and waterhammer when full steam pressure is applied, particularly if a direct lift of the condensate after the trap is attempted.

It is far better to use a number of smaller batteries in series rather than one large one, arranging for automatic temperature controls to bring each in in turn as the load increases. Unless there is always sufficient pressure at the trap outlet to overcome any lift, condensate should be drained by gravity to a vented receiver and lifted into the overhead return by an automatic pump.

When heater batteries are in series, each should be treated as a separate unit and should not under any circumstances be group trapped, because the load and pressure condition in each are likely to be so different. Figure 104 shows a typical layout.

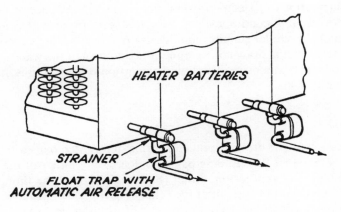

Figure 104

Kitchen equipment

Tea kettles

There are two types of tea kettle: instantaneous heaters, and storage. In their steam trapping problems they resemble the two types of hot water calorifier already described, but they are very much smaller.

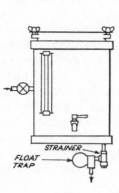

Figure 105

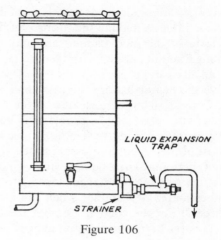

Figure 106

In the instantaneous heater kettle, steam consumption is either nothing or it is a maximum. A small float trap is probably the best type to use (Figure 105) but a balanced pressure thermostatic or a thermodynamic trap can also be fitted. The balanced pressure thermostatic trap should be mounted at the end of a 1 m cooling leg.

The storage type kettle has a reservoir of water always on the boil. There are no great fluctuations in steam consumption. The steam space is large and is oversized for running conditions, so as to be able to provide reasonably quick heating from cold. Under running conditions there is therefore excessive boiling when no water is being drawn off. Temperature control of the water is desirable, but is apt to be too expensive. The liquid expansion type of trap is indicated for this job (Figure 106).

Boiling pans

A full discussion on the draining and air venting of jacketed pans will be found in Chapter 7 (pages 118–23). Boiling pans in kitchens are either of the fixed type with side steam inlet and bottom outlet (Figure 107), or of the tilting type with steam in at one trunnion and out at the other (Figure 108). Steam consumption is heavy when starting from cold and very light when up to heat.

The jacket is initially full of air, and a balanced pressure air vent will speed up the boil of 130 litres of soup by about 20 minutes. If the running of the kitchen will allow any advantage to be taken of this, fit one of these air vents; leave it off if this sort of time saving cannot be efficiently utilized. The arrangement of steam inlet and condensate outlet is, however, such that not all the air in the jacket reaches the trap, but forms a pocket at the top of the jacket opposite the steam inlet. Space is usually an important consideration in kitchen layouts, and steam traps of a type which can be supported on the pipework are a distinct advantage, as this arrangement leads to cleaner floors.

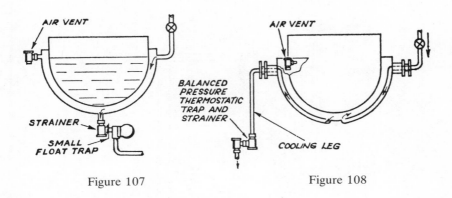

Figure 107   Figure 108

The choice of trap therefore lies between the float with thermostatic air release, the balanced pressure thermostatic or the inverted bucket. The float type is best, but it may be considered perhaps too good for the job (see Figure 107).

The thermostatic type is quite adequate but it must be properly installed about 1 m away from the outlet trunnion as shown in Figure 108. It should be protected by a strainer.

The inverted bucket trap can be used on these pans, but if so, it becomes more important to air vent the jacket if quick heating up is required. There remains the usual disadvantage: that this type of trap will be somewhat wasteful of steam on the low load conditions towards the end of the boil.

Wet steaming ovens

Traps on wet steaming ovens come in for more blame than almost any other piece of equipment in some kitchens. Figure 109 shows a typical oven of this type installed in a way that was by no means uncommon at one time. The steam feed is overhead at A at 35 kPa from a reducing valve. A branch line B comes down to a three-way inlet and vent cock C, interconnected to the opening handle on the steamer door. This makes it impossible for the door to be opened when the oven is full of steam (or should do so; but sometimes the handle has been taken off and put back in the wrong position).

The compartments may be individually trapped or all connected to one large combined float trap and grease box (not shown) but these are no longer in common use.

The prepared food is put into any or all of the three compartments of the oven, the door is shut and steam is turned on at C. Now while C has been shut off, steam has been condensing in the pipe B, so the first thing that comes into the oven when C is opened is about half a litre of water which sprays over the food. Steamed puddings in particular resent this treatment. Even when this initial deluge has passed, the steam is still likely to be very wet because the pipe B is tapped off the bottom of the main A and will act as a condensate drain point.

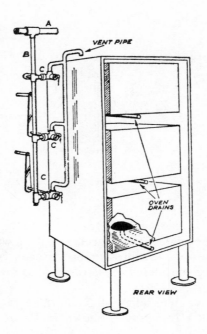

Figure 109

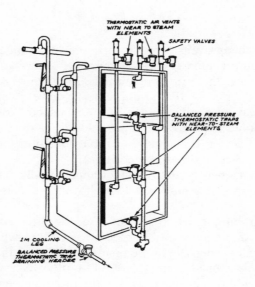

Figure 110

The compartments are full of air when C is opened. This air may or may not get out according to the relative positions of the steam inlet and drain outlet to each compartment and the type of steam trapping. If the air remains it will slow up the cooking. Steam condenses and the water flows through a strainer in the bottom of the compartment to the steam trap. The strainer is to prevent pieces of food getting in the outlet pipe and blocking it. If grease is present, depending on the food being cooked, it will pass through the steam trap with the condensate and be separated out in some form of grease trap.

Figure 110 shows the correct way of draining and air venting a steaming oven. The steam supply is taken off the top of the main and the bottom of the header is drained by a balanced-pressure thermostatic trap fitted at the end of 1 m of cooling leg.

Each compartment is drained by a balanced-pressure trap having a near-to-steam element and fitted as near as possible to each outlet, with no pipe strainers. Grease runs out when some foods are being cooked and this grease must be passed through the system hot, before it has time to congeal and block the outlet pipes. These pipes should be in straight lengths with cleaning plugs at any change of direction.

Each compartment is also fitted with a balanced-pressure air vent with near-to-steam element because of the importance of complete air removal.

Even when these precautions have been studied, steaming ovens can still cause trouble. The oven makers recommend that steam should be turned on for a while before any food is put in and that the oven should be blown through again after cooking is finished. This is to clear the pipes of grease. Caustic should not be used for cleaning, otherwise the trap and air vent elements will be damaged by corrosion. The strainers in the bottoms of the compartments are there to prevent food getting down the outlet pipes, but some misguided cooks have the habit of taking out the strainer and poking any loose pieces down the hole. It is supposed to be a quick way of cleaning. The oven should be cleaned with the strainers in position and broken strainers should be at once replaced.

Indirect steaming ovens

There are other types of oven which generate their own steam as shown in Figure 111. A steam coil runs round a water bath in the base of the oven. Steam

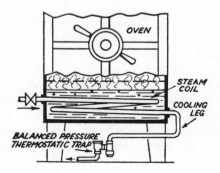

Figure 111

is generated and rises up into the compartments above. Such an arrangement disposes of all grease troubles and the condensate from the trap is suitable for boiler feed. From the steam trapping point of view such an oven is only a small coil heated hot water tank. The trap fitted may be of almost any type – inverted bucket, float or balanced pressure thermostatic. A small and inexpensive one will probably be chosen because the job is small and simple, but a strainer is advisable. If a balanced pressure thermostatic trap is preferred it should be fitted at the end of a 1 m cooling leg.

Hot plates

These can be treated as radiators, having a large steam space compared with their heat transmission. Their trap requirements are simple and can best be met with a balanced pressure thermostatic trap fitted close so as to use some of the Specific enthalpy of water (Figure 112).

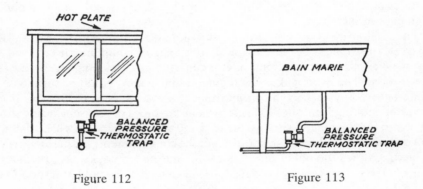

Figure 112   Figure 113

Bain maries

These too should have the same treatment as steam heated radiators and be fitted with traps similar to the hot plate recommendation (Figure 113).

Hospital equipment

Steam heated sterilizers and disinfectors are the only special pieces of steam equipment common to hospitals, other than those already discussed in this chapter. They are of many types from simple instrument sterilizers to the elaborate ones found in operating theatres. These latter are fitted with steam, air and vacuum supplied with automatic control and a clearly defined cycle of operations. They differ widely between one make and another and no general recommendation about steam trapping or air venting can be laid down, even if this were desirable.

Instrument sterilizers

These are, in effect, small water tanks heated with a steam coil. It is important that there should be no waterlogging, because the coil is short, but should be able to give quick heating up. The trap chosen should be small and is generally required with a polished nickel or chrome finish and no dirt collecting corners. One of the balanced pressure thermostatic type answers best to this description and it should be fitted at the end of a 1 m cooling leg (Figure 114).

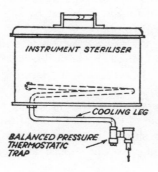

Figure 114

Utensil sterilizers

The sterilizing of utensils is sometimes carried out in a closed vessel heated with live steam. On this particular job air removal has great importance. The presence of air in the vessel will mean that the sterilizer temperature is below that corresponding to the pressure gauge reading. But it is essential that the correct temperature should be reached and held for the required time. An automatic air vent with near-to-steam element should be fitted at a point remote from the steam inlet. The amount of condensate formed in these sterilizers is not great and the steam pressure is generally low. A plated trap and strainer of the balanced pressure type with a near-to-steam element, so that it can be fitted close under the unit, is the most convenient (Figure 115).

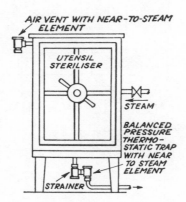

Figure 115

Dressing sterilizers, disinfectors, disinfestors

These vary considerably in size but, in general, they are steam jacketed vessels and the material to be sterilized is loaded into the chamber where it is brought into direct contact with live steam for a period of time sufficient to kill all bacteria.

It is literally a matter of life or death that sterilization should be complete and fully automatic high vacuum sterilizers have been developed to achieve this. They are supplied complete with the trapping and air venting equipment which the manufacturer has found to give the best results and it is not advisable to make changes without his agreement.

We will describe a typical sterilizer, which was in common use before the advent of the high-vacuum units, because it illustrates the general principles of steam sterilization and will allow those still operating these units to get the best from them. Figure 116 shows a typical unit.

Proper sterilization depends on the steam being able to penetrate the load completely so that the whole of it is brought up to the correct temperature. For this to happen the steam should be saturated and all air must be rapidly removed. If the steam is either wet or superheated proper sterilization will not take place.

Steam should be brought to the sterilizer at boiler pressure and a reducing valve fitted close to the unit to reduce the pressure to that required for

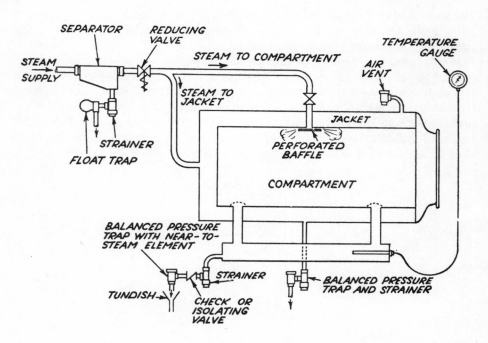

Figure 116

sterilization. A separator, drained by a small float trap, should be fitted just before the reducing valve. In this position it will not only dry the steam entering the chamber but will prevent wear of the reducing valve caused by the erosive action of wet steam. All pipes should be adequately sized so that the chamber comes up to full pressure as quickly as possible after steam is turned on.

The pressure in the jacket should be the same as that in the chamber to prevent the steam in the latter becoming superheated with the possibility of damaging the load and preventing sterilization.

Condensate is drained from the jacket by a balanced pressure thermostatic trap protected by a strainer. Air venting of the jacket will depend on the position of the steam inlet; if this is at the top the air will probably be removed satisfactory by the trap but if it is at the bottom or one end as shown in Figure 116 then a separate thermostatic air vent will be needed.

Proper air and condensate removal from the chamber is of the highest importance. For rapid air removal with the minimum of mixing it is preferable for steam to be introduced at the top of the chamber, so that it can displace the air downwards to outlets at the bottom. Drain holes at least 50 mm in diameter and covered with a wire mesh screen, should be provided and connected to a manifold of the same diameter into which the displaced air can pass and be discharged by a balanced pressure trap fitted with a near-to-steam element.

As well as discharging the air originally filling the chamber, a trap of this type will open to let out air which is slowly driven out of the interstices of the load during the sterilizing process.

This trap will, of course, also discharge condensate from the chamber and should be protected by a strainer from any dirt or fibrous material from dressings which might otherwise block up the trap orifice.

If a vacuum is pulled on the chamber at the end of the sterilizing cycle to dry the load by flashing off any residual moisture, some form of isolating valve will be needed to prevent air being sucked in through the steam trap and Figure 116 shows a check valve fitted for this purpose.

Two further points should be mentioned. First of all, the temperature in the chamber should be measured by an accurate thermometer with the bulb positioned at the lowest point of the steam space, which is usually the condensate manifold. Secondly, if a vacuum is pulled on the chamber at the end of the cycle it is imperative that the air drawn into the chamber when this vacuum is broken should not be contaminated in any way. For this reason the trap draining the chamber should never be connected directly into the waste system. Some form of 'air break' such as an open tundish, should be used.

7 Pans, evaporators and storage tanks

Jacketed pans

Although jacketed pans are used in many industries, they are found in their widest variety in the manufacture of food and confectionery. A consideration of the draining and air venting of the pans in use in this industry does indeed cover all types, except the largest.

The practice of draining condensate from jacketed pans through plug cocks used to be common, and there are some people who still use this method. Those who do say that steam traps are unsatisfactory because they slow up production. On certain cooking processes speed is of paramount importance and any slowing-up affects the quality of the product. There is no doubt that some users of jacketed pans speak from experience when they decry the use of steam traps. The reason is worth examining.

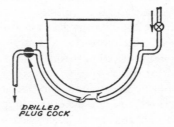

DRILLED
PLUG COCK

Figure 117

Figure 117 shows a jacketed pan of a type commonly used in the manufacture of jam. Steam is admitted through one trunnion and passes down a pipe, or passage in the casting, to the bottom. Condensate is forced up a syphon pipe, or cored passage, to the outlet trunnion and so through a drilled cock. When steam is turned on, a considerable proportion of the air in the jacket is forced out through the cock. There is no possibility of steam locking in the syphon pipe. There must always be a certain velocity through the steam space, because of the valve opening. The use of a drilled cock has, therefore, eliminated any possibility of air binding and steam locking, has materially lowered the percentage of air in the jacket, and has created a certain velocity over the surfaces of heat transference. But these good effects are obtained only by having a hole

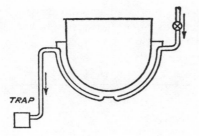

Figure 118

sufficiently large to discharge condensate at the peak rate under starting conditions. For perhaps 80 % of the cooking time there is a waste of live steam.

In an attempt to cut out this steam loss, a trap is fitted (Figure 118) on the floor by the pan. The trap has no automatic provision for venting air or for releasing locked steam. When steam is turned on, the jacket and syphon pipe are full of air and no condensate can reach the trap which is air bound. An air vent of some kind is therefore essential on the trap. Suppose it is a hand operated vent – when this is opened the air in the syphon pipe is driven out and, since we are trying to save steam, the vent is closed when steam begins to blow from it. Then will follow another period during which condensate is not discharged, because the trap is steam locked. In time the locked steam will condense and the trap will operate to discharge the condensate which has meanwhile been waterlogging the steam space. Unless steam locking is understood, it is more than likely that this waterlogging will be put down to the fact that the trap has insufficient capacity to handle the starting load. This may lead to the fitting of a by-pass round the trap. The operator will then find that he gets quicker cooking if the by-pass is left a bit open. In other words, he will have proved that an orifice is better than a steam trap.

On the other hand a trap with a steam lock release may be fitted. The release is adjusted so that it will dissipate the steam from the syphon pipe. The trap is fitted as close to the trunnion as possible. There is no loss of live steam by this method – remember that the use*less* steam in the syphon pipe is separated from the use*ful* steam in the steam space by the condensate that is following the locked steam up the pipe; but there is no hold up at the trap.

In spite of the fitting of this special trap, it is still found that cooking times are longer than those with the orifice method. This is because we are losing the good effect of the continual steam velocity, which drove out some of the initial air and improved heat transference. The next step is to fit a thermostatic air vent at the top of the jacket preferably on the side opposite to the steam inlet. This air vent will be wide open when steam is turned on and a very large proportion of the initial air will be swept out.

It will be found that a complete installation of steam lock release trap and air vent will give a cooking time a trifle better than the plug cock or orifice method due to the higher pressure maintained in the jacket. The steam saving will be considerable.

The table which follows is a record of actual tests which have been made using a variety of pans and methods of condensate removal. The loss of production due to steam trapping without complementary air venting is very noticeable.

	time		time saved	steam saved
	min.	sec.		
extra rapid (jelly)				
Correct trapping and air venting	3	45	nil	24.3 %
Fixed orifice	3	45	–	–
rapid (jam)				
Correct trapping and air venting	10	3	4.3 %	21.7 %
Correct trapping, no air venting	11	0	lost 4.8 %	9.2 %
Fixed orifice	10	30	–	–
slow (soup – large pan)				
Correct trapping and air venting	18	0	26 %	25.2 %
Correct trapping, no air venting	28	30	lost 17 %	16.8 %
Fixed orifice	24	20	–	–
slow (toffee – small pan)				
Correct trapping and air venting	31	42	7.9 %	15.2 %

Slow boiling pans

Figure 119 shows a small fixed pan with a diameter below, say, 600 mm and with a bottom outlet. Boiling time is slow – from perhaps 20 to 40 minutes. The condensation rate is not heavy, but will be considerably greater on starting. Steam locking is not a serious matter if the trap is fitted close to the outlet. The trap chosen for the job can be either a small float trap (with automatic air

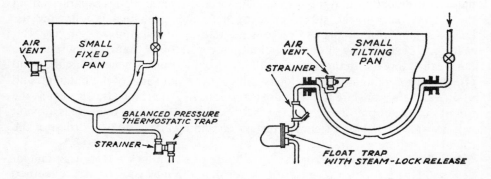

Figure 119   Figure 120

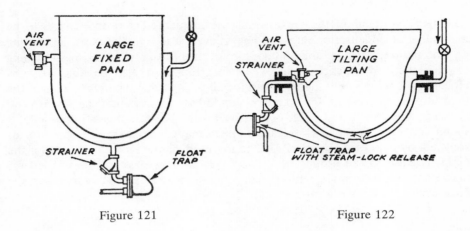

Figure 121   Figure 122

release), a thermodynamic trap, an inverted bucket trap or a balanced pressure thermostatic trap. If the last named is chosen it should be fitted about 1 m away from the outlet (this does not lead to undue steam locking, because the length of pipe is a water collector). A thermostatic air vent should be fitted as shown, as also should a strainer.

Figure 120 shows a pan of similar size and for about the same boiling time but with trunnion steam inlet and outlet. The problem is much the same except that steam locking is bound to occur however near the trap may be fitted. The best choice is, therefore, the float type with steam lock release. Air vent and strainer positions are as shown.

Figure 121 shows a fixed pan with bottom outlet, similar to Figure 119 except in size. This is a larger type. Boiling time is still 20 to 40 minutes. The condensate rate in this pan is greater and the peak rate on starting may be considerable, although the final rate is likely to be low. The need for an air vent is greater than ever, because of the depth of the jacket. Steam locking is not of great moment, providing the trap is fitted close to the outlet. If this is impossible, then special provision must be made at the trap. Any trap chosen must be able to vent air. The first choice is the float trap, but the thermodynamic type is a useful alternative, particularly where the outlet is close to the ground. Inverted bucket traps can also be used. A thermostatic trap is probably ruled out on the score of capacity.

Figure 122 shows a large tilting pan with trunnion inlet and outlet, similar to Figure 120 except in size. Boiling time is still 20 to 40 minutes. The problem of steam locking here becomes acute because of the increased volume of the syphon pipe and the speed at which waterlogging can occur. The float type with special steam lock release is indicated. The air vent position remains as before.

Quick boiling pans

We will now consider pans in which the boiling process lasts only 5 to 15 minutes. Waterlogging, and air binding, and reduced heat transference, due to the presence of air in the jacket, must be eliminated if production is to be maintained. Condensation rates are heavy, even in the smaller pans, on starting up, and the trap must be able to take care of this. But there is only light loading towards the end of each cycle, when the trap must also be able to work efficiently. Undoubtedly the best trap for all pans of this type is once again the float trap. In the case of a fixed pan it should have an automatic air release and be fitted close up to the drain point (see Figure 121). If this is impossible, it should have both steam lock release and automatic air release or a separate air vent in a by-pass (see Figure 123). The thermodynamic type can be used if the outlet is close to the ground but an air vent in a by-pass will be needed for maximum production. On a tilting pan a steam lock release is essential and the arrangement is shown in Figure 124.

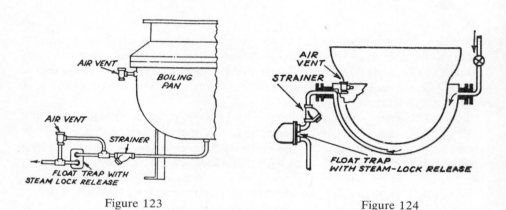

Figure 123   Figure 124

Except in size a quick boiling pan with bottom outlet is similar to that shown in Figure 121 and a tilting pan with bottom steam inlet and syphon outlet is similar to that shown in Figure 120. Figure 124 is of a tilting pan with top steam inlet and syphon outlet.

Extra rapid pans

In order to provide extra heating surface, some pans are fitted with a coil as well as a jacket. Sometimes the steam for the coil is taken from the jacket and condensate is returned to the jacket, as shown in Figure 125. The trapping and air venting of such pans is on exactly the same lines as for similar pans without coils.

When the coil is fed with steam from the inlet trunnion and discharges into the outlet trunnion, conditions are different. Such pans are designed to discharge condensate (and live steam) through an orifice (Figure 117). Unless there is a flow through the outlet trunnion, condensate does not effectively drain from the coil. If such pans are trapped the coil will probably waterlog and the production of the pan will be seriously reduced. On the other hand, the steam wastage from

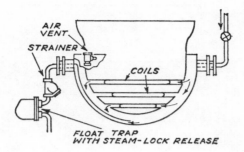

Figure 125

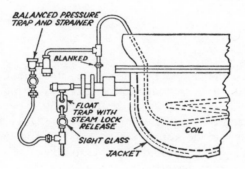

Figure 126

these pans is considerable. There is a way of getting both production and economy if a small alteration is made to the coil arrangement. Figure 126 shows the outlet from the coil blanked off from the trunnion and led away through an elbow to a separate steam trap. The method has proved most satisfactory in practice.

Residual steam

After correct steam trapping and air venting has been applied to a pan which previously discharged through an orifice, it is sometimes found difficult to control the end of the boil. When the orifice is in use, it is only necessary to shut off the inlet valve. Any residual steam passes away through the hole. If the outlet is trapped, this residual steam remains and goes on giving up heat to the process. Sometimes this does not matter, because the process material is run out or tipped out at once. At other times it may cause trouble.

There are three simple ways of overcoming the difficulty; these are shown in Figure 127. A three-way plug cock can be fitted on the steam inlet; in one position, steam is conected to the jacket; in the other, the jacket is connected to

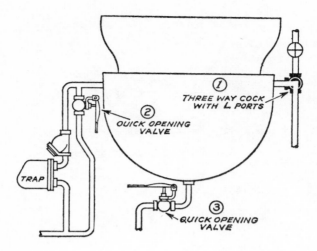

Figure 127

the condensate return line (1). An isolating valve should be fitted above the plug cock for closing during long stoppages, plug cocks not being too reliable.

A spring-loaded quick release valve can be arranged between the trunnion and the condensate return, parallel to the steam trap (2). This valve is held shut by the spring and has to be kept open by hand during the blow down. An ordinary valve in this position would be liable to abuse.

A quick release valve can easily be fitted from the bottom drain of a fixed pan (3). This too is in parallel with the steam trap.

Of the three methods the first is the simplest; but the plug cock must be a good one.

Pan maintenance

Unless the makers of the pan have provided a vent hole in the jacket, some trouble may be experienced in fitting the thermostatic air vent. In a cast iron pan it is only a matter of drilling and tapping. In a copper or aluminium or steel pan it means brazing on or welding on a boss. It is not a bad idea, when ordering a new pan, to ask the manufacturer to put this on for you.

If you have to make the hole yourself, you have the consolation of knowing that the presence of the hole will greatly simplify hydraulic testing for the factory inspector.

The best position for the air vent can easily be found by filling the pan with water, turning on steam and bringing the water to the boil.

The rate of boiling of the water in contact with the jacket will be noticeably less where a pocket of air has collected.

The most important part of a jacketed pan is the steam condensing surface. The condition of this surface has a considerable bearing on the performance of the pan. Many firms, whose output depends largely on pan production, have a regular maintenance routine of polishing this condensing surface every few weeks. The reason which lies behind this practice, is that steam may condense on a surface in two ways, either in a thin film of water or in separate drops of water. The condition of the surface, other things being equal, determines the method of condensation. Drop condensation allows from five to ten times the heat transference of film condensation – presumably because of the easier access of new steam to the metal surface. A polished, slightly greasy surface causes drop condensation and on a rough, pitted surface the film effect takes place. The ideal surface for the outside (i.e. condensing surface) of a jacketed pan is chrome plate on polished copper, wiped over with an oily rag (but not mineral oil, it should be castor oil or rancid butter).

It should be noted that these remarks apply only to the steam side of the metal. On the process material side, heat is being transferred from the wall to the material and conditions are quite different; at one stage in the boiling of the process material there is even an advantage in having a rough, non-greasy metal surface. Make sure, though, that the material being heated does not bake onto the metal surface because the resulting film will be highly resistant to heat transference.

The outside surface of the pan, which is exposed to the air, is, on the other hand, a source of heat loss. If this is of iron, the heat loss by radiation from the surface can be reduced by as much as 40 % by painting with metallic aluminium paint.

Coil heated vessels

The time taken to heat up a vessel by means of submerged pipe coils depends upon: the area of the coil surface; the temperature head across the wall; the velocity of steam and the liquid across the surfaces; the nature of the surfaces; and the presence of insulating films on both the steam and the liquid sides of the wall. If the function of the coil is to heat material in the quickest possible time and then to carry out an evaporation process, all the factors which influence heat transference must be kept as favourable as possible. If, on the other hand, the function of the coil is to heat process material and then to maintain it at a certain temperature, it should be possible to vary the heat transference from the coil. During the heating stage this should be as rapid as possible; during the period of heat maintenance the heat transference should be reduced.

The job which the vessel has to do is thus seen to determine the design of steam coil, the method of feeding steam to the coil and the method of taking air and condensate away from it. Perhaps these examples will illustrate the practical application of the principle.

Large concentrating vessels

Figure 128 shows a large brewing copper in which liquor has to be heated up and concentrated by a heater and base coil. For output both should have the

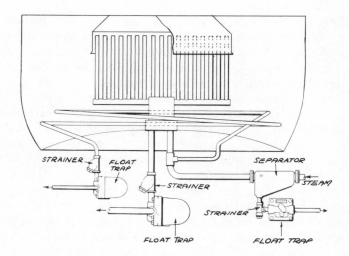

Figure 128

greatest possible heat transference. The load on these coppers is generally a very large part of the brewery steam requirements and the setting-on of a copper often causes a considerable drop in the available steam pressure. This fact must be realized and the steam traps chosen for the heater and coil must be capable of discharging the heavy starting load at the reduced starting pressure.

The pressure drop in the heater is greater than the pressure drop in the coil, so that the two units must each be drained through their own steam trap. The coil in the copper must be given a proper fall to the outlet, or waterhammer will take place due to the heavy condensation. Because of this heavy loading it is advisable that both coil and heater traps are fitted close to the outlets of the units; even a momentary steam locking will cause waterlogging and a reduction in the boil.

Air will certainly have to be discharged in considerable quantities, because brewing is a batch process and the steam spaces fill with air between whiles and because the high condensation rate will leave air behind uncondensed.

For all these reasons large-sized float traps with inbuilt thermostatic air vents are by far the best choice. The only possible alternative would be inverted bucket traps with separate air by-passes; but these, because of their blast discharge action on the small steam spaces of the heater, have been known to cause irregular boiling.

Batch stills

The difference between the brewing vessel just considered and a steam heated still is simply that in the former vapour is driven off (although not perhaps wasted, see page 95) and the desired product is left in the vessel, while in the latter the vapour which is driven off is itself the desired product.

The type of still most closely resembling the brewing vessel is a simple batch still. The liquid to be distilled is run in cold, steam is turned on, the liquid is heated to the boiling point of the required product, the addition of more heat from the steam evaporates the liquid by adding Specific enthalpy of evaporation to it, the vapours are collected and cooled, residues are run out of the vessel and the cycle is complete.

Heat transference from the coil must be as good as possible if production is to be maintained. The starting rate of condensation is considerably higher than the finishing rate; but it is while the liquor is boiling that heat transference is of vital importance because then the available temperature head between the steam and the liquor is least.

In many distillation processes the maintenance of steady temperatures is desirable to obtain uniformity and purity of the product. Sometimes the steam inlet to the still is automatically controlled by a sensitive thermostat. This special requirement can affect the choice of steam trap.

One of the recommendations given for the brewing vessel was an inverted bucket trap. These traps, in general, give an intermittent or blast discharge. If the heating surface in the still is large in relation to the volume of steam, and if the quantity of liquor in the still is small, an intermittent discharge trap should be avoided. The scouring action when the trap discharges will, under these conditions, cause an alteration in the rate of heat transference, which is undesirable. A continuous discharge float trap is a better choice for this work.

If the steam space is large and volume of liquid being distilled is great, such a blast discharge will have no practical effect and, as an alternative to the float trap, the inverted bucket trap is suitable on a large still and a thermodynamic

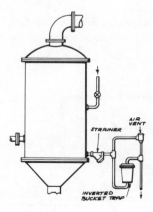

Figure 129

trap on a small still. Even more care than usual should however be taken to avoid steam locking or air binding. Either of these can cause irregularities of heat transference which are much greater than the blast discharge effect referred to. The exact arrangement of coil will determine the air venting position; but unless the steam pipes are arranged in some parallel formation with steam and condensate headers, it is probable that the drain point will also be the air vent point. In such a case a separate thermostatic air by-pass round the trap is indicated – Figure 129.

Continuous stills

Continuous stills differ from the batch still only insofar as the feed of liquor to the vessel is continuous and is likely to be preheated in a separate vessel. Since the coil in the still is called on to provide mainly Specific enthalpy of evaporation to the liquor, conditions are steadier. If all the preheating is done by a separate steam supply, even the starting load is light, but if the preheating is done by the heat in the vapours from the still, the starting load will be heavier. This point should be remembered in choosing the steam trap, which must, of course, have a capacity sufficient to handle the amount of condensate formed under the worst conditions.

As before, steam locking and air binding of the trap are likely to have bad effects on the distillation process and care must be taken to prevent them. A blast discharge trap may or may not be a drawback. The safest choice is a float trap (fitted close to the outlet if possible, otherwise with a steam lock release).

Air venting of the coils should be taken care of by a thermostatic air vent. Figure 130 shows a typical arrangement of trapping and air venting with float traps on a benzolized oil preheater and continuous benzol still.

Constant temperature heaters

In many vessels a steam coil is used to heat liquid up to a set temperature and to maintain it at that temperature, perhaps indefinitely, perhaps for a given time.

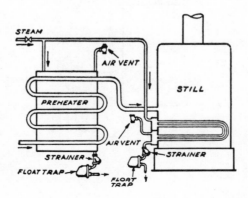

Figure 130

The amount of heat required from the coil during the warming up period is greater than the amount required when the liquid is up to temperature and only losing heat by radiation. It may be that, when the liquid is hot, cold articles are immersed in it. This calls for a further supply of heat from the coil and this demand may indeed be greater than the initial warming up demand; in which case the coil will have been designed on this basis.

In such vessels the heat transference from the coil must be capable of variation. A valve can be fitted on the steam inlet which is automatically opened or shut according to the temperature of the liquor. The partial closing of this valve will reduce the steam pressure in the coil, so decreasing the temperature head, and will also decrease the velocity of steam over the surface.

On the other hand a liquid expansion steam trap can be fitted on the outlet from the coil. When the liquor is hot the condensate in the coil is hot, the trap is partly shut and condensate is held back. This lowers the heat transference of the coil by reducing the effective area and by increasing the resistant film of water.

Because the automatic valve is actuated directly by the water temperature, there is an immediate response to any change of conditions. The steam trap on the other hand responds only to changes at second hand. If temperature conditions are liable to sudden alterations, and it is important that such alterations should be quickly corrected, automatic control at the inlet valve is essential. The steam trap control is of value when temperature fluctuations are slow and their effects not very important.

If an automatic temperature controlled valve is fitted at the inlet, the steam trap chosen for the outlet must be of a type which discharges condensate at steam temperature and if the steam coil is sized to heat the liquor up quickly it is best that it should not blast-discharge a large volume of condensate at a time. For example, if the trap were to cause condensate to be held up in the coil, even temporarily, the liquor temperature would begin to drop and the inlet valve would open to admit more steam; the trap would in due course discharge and clear the coil, the steam supply would be too great and the valve would begin to

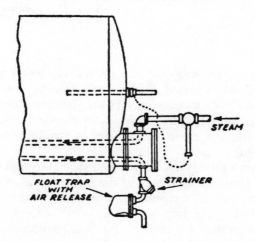

Figure 131

close down. This 'hunting' of the control valve would occur when there was no natural change of temperature in the liquor and no real need for the control to come into operation. A similar condition is set up when a trap discharges a large volume of condensate in one blast.

Similar hunting of the temperature control is caused by air binding and steam locking. If the condensate rate is heavy, the most satisfactory trap to use is the continuous discharge float type, and if it is light inverted bucket or thermodynamic traps can be used as alternatives to the float trap – the usual precautions against steam locking and air binding being taken. Figure 131 shows a temperature controlled vessel with continuous discharge trap and thermostatic air release.

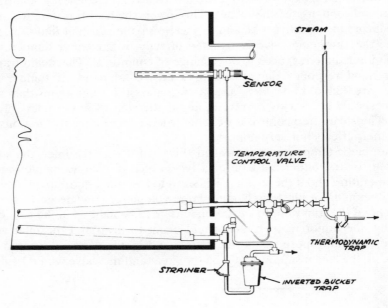

Figure 132

In the case of large storage tanks, however, the liquor temperature changes only slowly and an inverted bucket trap can be used to withstand the waterhammer which often occurs in very long heating coils. Figure 132 shows a typical oil storage tank installation in which the steam supply is drained by a thermodynamic trap and an air vent is fitted in parallel with the inverted bucket trap on the heating coil.

Figure 133 shows an oil tank heated by a steam coil and drained with a liquid expansion trap. If accurate control of the oil temperature is not required and since there are no sudden temperature variations in the oil, a sufficiently exact control is obtained by the trap holding up condensate when the oil is hot and releasing it all when the oil is cold and full heat transference is wanted from the coil. A bimetallic trap could also be used.

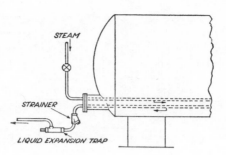

STEAM

STRAINER

LIQUID EXPANSION TRAP

Figure 133

Multiple effect evaporators

The brewing vessel considered under the heading 'Large concentrating vessels' is a single effect evaporator. Such a process is fundamentally wasteful if the Specific enthalpy of water in the concentrated liquor and the Specific enthalpies of water and evaporation in the vapour are not put to use. The continuous still is (from the heat conservation angle) an improvement if the vapour is used to preheat the liquor. But even so the heat extracted from the vapour is only sufficient to give Specific enthalpy of water to the liquor. Multiple effect evaporation is a means of saving some of the Specific enthalpy of water from the concentrated liquor and some of the Specific enthalpy of steam from the vapour. It is a method which will always be considered by the seeker after process heat efficiency.

If heat losses are neglected, it takes the heat from rather more than one kilogram of steam to evaporate one kilogram of water in a single effect evaporator. But, theoretically, the energy required to evaporate a kilogram of water is very much less than the total energy available in a kilogram of steam. For example the energy required to evaporate a kilogram of water from a 10 % glycerine solution is the equivalent of only 74 kJ.

Multiple effect evaporation consists of a series of evaporators, each working at a lower pressure than the one before. The concentrated liquor from one is pumped hot to the next and flash vapour from one passes over to the heating tubes of the next and gives up heat to the concentrate at its new lower temperature, thus generating more vapour and giving greater concentration with no additional outside heat.

If the initial pressure is high, the succeeding effects may all be at positive but lower gauge pressures. If the initial pressure is low, succeeding effects may be obtained by the use of vacuum pumps.

Since, theoretically, one kilogram of vapour will evaporate nearly one kilogram of liquor in each stage of the process and only one kilogram of steam is used to start the cycle, it is obvious that great heat economies are possible with the multiple effect process.

Figure 134 shows a typical layout of a low pressure multiple effect evaporator. The condenser after C puts a vacuum on the vapour space in C reducing the

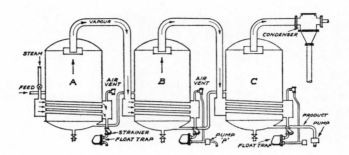

Figure 134

absolute pressure to 15 kPa and liquor in C boils at 54 °C. The concentrate is pumped out. The heating medium in the tubes of C is the vapour from B. This is at the pressure of the B vapour space, say, 37 kPa absolute and a temperature of 74 °C. The liquor from B is pumped to C and is given extra heat because of the 20 °C head across the C tubes.

The heating medium in the tubes of B is the vapour from A. This is at the pressure of the A vapour space, say 70 kPa absolute and a temperature of 90 °C. The liquor from A is pumped to B and is given extra heat because of the 16 °C head across the B tubes.

The heating medium in the A tubes is steam at a pressure of, say, 20 kPa gauge and a temperature of 105 °C. This is the sole external source of heat for the whole process.

For simplicity the boiling point of water alone is taken in each case. In practice, of course, the boiling point of the solution increases as the concentration increases and the temperature difference between the vapour and the liquor being heated is decreased correspondingly.

The correct draining and air venting of the A, B and C tubes has a profound effect on the process. Suppose, for example, that the drain trap on C air binds. Condensate is held up in the C tubes which cannot deliver their scheduled amount of heat. The pressure drop of the vapour in the C tubes is reduced, so the pressure of the vapour in B increases. This reduces the temperature head across the B tubes, reduces the heat transference across the B tubes, reduces the pressure drop in them, increases the vapour pressure in A, reduces the temperature head across the A tubes. Evaporation from the whole process is thus completely upset by a trivial happening to the steam trap at C.

Condensate in the tubes of A is under slight pressure and the trap will discharge normally. If the condensate is led to a flash tank, the steam generated can be fed to the tubes of B or C to increase the available heat supply.

Condensate in the tubes of B and C and flash tank (if fitted) is under vacuum and must be pumped. This can be done either by a separate pump system, and the condensate saved (if clean), or by connecting the outlets to the condenser and the condensate wasted.

The air vents on the B and C effects must also discharge into the same vacuum line.

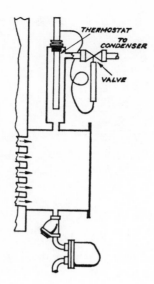

Figure 135

The vapour in B and C tubes may contain dissolved corrosive gases and this point must be watched in considering traps and air vents which will have to be made of corrosion resisting materials. On very big evaporators the amount of air to be discharged may be too much for a normal air vent to handle and the method shown in Figure 135 would be worth considering. The automatic temperature controlled valve is operated by a sensitive thermostat bulb mounted in a corrosion resistant pocket.

The steam traps chosen should have ample capacity, be free from air binding and steam locking troubles, should not have a heavy blast-discharge action and should discharge condensate at steam temperature. This points to the float trap as the best recommendation.

Evaporators as reducing valves

The interesting way in which an evaporator can be made to do the work of a desuperheater and a reducing valve, and more efficiently than either, can best be shown by considering a practical example.

A works generates steam for power at, say, 1200 kPa and 260 °C total temperature (68 °C Superheat). There is no process steam requirement, but it is desired to put in a canteen which needs saturated steam at 70 kPa. Can the high pressure steam be used, or must a separate and comparatively inefficient boiler plant be installed?

Figure 136 shows an evaporator arranged to take high pressure steam as a heating medium. This imparts heat to water in the vessel, the water evaporating and setting up a pressure of saturated steam as required. The flow of high pressure steam must be automatically controlled by the pressure in the

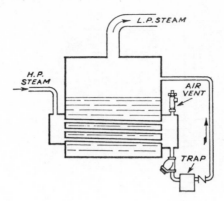

Figure 136

evaporator, so that it can maintain it at a constant set amount. Condensate from the tubes is passed through the trap to the vapour space where some of it flashes into low pressure steam, the hot condensate helps to make up the supply of water required for evaporation. The only heat loss by the process is from the outside surfaces of the evaporator and this is reduced to a very small amount by efficient lagging.

In this particular case the trap should be of a mechanical type suitable for superheat, preferably having a continuous discharge and passing condensate at steam temperature.

Film evaporators

Some liquids foam badly when they are boiled and advantage is taken of this fact in film evaporators. These may be either of the falling film type as shown in Figure 137 or the climbing film type as shown in Figure 138. Both have the big advantage that the material is only in contact with the heat for a short time which reduces the danger of overheating.

The falling film evaporator consists of a double bank of vertical stacked steam jacketed pipes. Each section is individually trapped as shown, because as the liquid falls its boiling point rises due to concentration, the temperature head is reduced, and the pressure drop through each steam jacket is progressively less.

The starting load on such evaporators is not appreciably greater than the running load, but it is possible to make considerable fluctuation in the rate of liquor flow. For maximum output and smooth operation a trap which discharges continuously at steam temperature is desirable, so it is best to use a float trap with inbuilt air release.

The climbing film evaporator shown in Figure 138 consists of a vessel in which the liquor is fed up to the level A. This is heated by steam round the tubes. As the liquor boils, the film climbs the tubes, evaporating on the way. The steam space is high and requires separate air venting at a remote point as shown. The type of trap chosen is not vital and preference is likely to fall on a float or

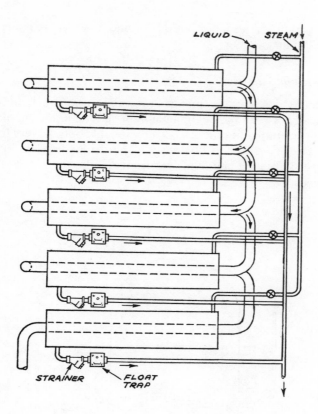

Figure 137

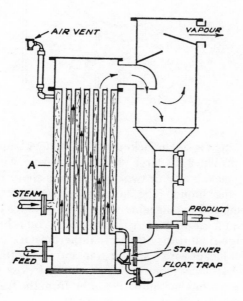

Figure 138

inverted bucket trap. The usual provisions should however be made to prevent steam locking and air binding.

Combined jacket and coil heating

The concentrating of certain liquids by evaporation demands that the temperature head between the heating medium and the liquid should always be low – milk is one example. In order to get a reasonable output, very large heating surfaces must be used and it is obviously of particular importance that these should be properly drained and kept free from air film.

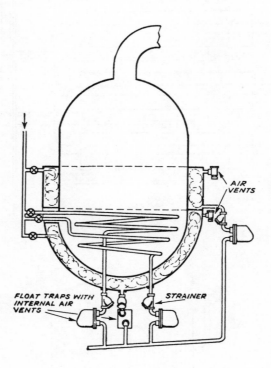

Figure 139

An evaporator which is steam jacketed and fitted with internal coils, as shown in Figure 139, provides a large heating surface without being unduly cumbersome. The jackets are in two sections and there may be two or three separate coils in the liquid. The heating surfaces are split up into these comparatively small and manageable sections in parallel just so that each one can be kept at the highest pitch of efficiency. Each coil is best drained through a continuous discharge float trap with internal thermostatic air vent fitted close to the outlet and each jacket with a similar trap and an additional air vent fitted at the top of the jacket away from the steam inlet. If low temperature vacuum steam is used as the heating medium, the outlet from the traps and air vents must of course be connected to a lower vacuum line.

8 Dryers

Drying efficiency

There is no fundamental difference between evaporating and drying processes. In both, the problem is to get rid of a certain amount of unwanted liquid. The fact that this amount is generally less in drying operations does, however, lead to the use of different equipment and to a rather different way of measuring results.

The output of a dryer is measured by the weight of dried product. The cost of drying depends upon the kilograms of steam used per kilogram of product dried. It is therefore common practice, and a common fallacy, to think of the efficiency of a dryer in terms of kilograms of steam used per kilogram of product dried.

For example, consider two machines making paper. Machine A makes 0.07 kg of paper per second and the steam consumption is 3.5 kg per kg of paper. Machine B makes 0.07 kg of paper per second and the steam consumption is 3.4 kg per kg of paper. On cost, B is making paper at a cheaper rate. But it does not at all follow from the figures given that B is the more efficient machine.

Steam is being delivered to these machines in order to evaporate the surplus water from the stuff. Suppose that machine A is being fed with stuff having 70 % moisture, which leaves the machine with 10 % moisture. Machine B stuff enters with 68 % moisture and leaves with 10 % moisture.

Consider Machine A:

There are 0.07 kg/s of material leaving 90 % bone dry. This is made up of $0.07 \times \dfrac{90}{100} = 0.063$ kg/s of bone dry material and $0.07 \times \dfrac{10}{100} \doteq 0.007$ kg/s of water. On entry this same 0.063 kg/s of bone dry material makes up only 30 % of the stuff, the remaining 70 % consisting of water.

$\therefore$ Weight of stuff $= 0.063 \times \dfrac{100}{30} = 0.21$ kg/s

and weight of water $= 0.21 - 0.063 = 0.147$ kg/s
Hence the weight of water evaporated $= 0.147 - 0.007 = 0.140$ kg/s
The machine uses 3.5 kg of steam per kg of product and there are 0.07 kg/s of product
$\therefore$ steam consumption $= 3.5 \times 0.07 = 0.245$ kg/s
$\therefore$ steam used per kg of water evaporated $= \dfrac{0.245}{0.14} = 1.75$ kg

Consider Machine B:

As before, there are 0.063 kg/s of bone dry material produced with 0.007 kg/s of water, but on entry there is 32 % of bone dry material and 68 % of water.

So 0.063 kg/s makes up 32 % of the weight of the stuff which $= 0.063 \times \dfrac{100}{32}$

$$= 0.197 \text{ kg/s}$$

$\therefore$ Weight of water $= 0.197 - 0.063 = 0.134$ kg/s

Hence the weight of water evaporated $= 0.134 - 0.007 = 0.127$ kg/s

Machine B uses 3.4 kg of steam per kg of product and there are 0.07 kg/s of product

$\therefore$ steam consumption $= 3.4 \times 0.07 = 0.238$ kg/s

$\therefore$ steam used per kg of water evaporated $= \dfrac{0.238}{0.127} = 1.87$ kg

Machine A is therefore doing a better job of work than Machine B, because it is using only 1.75 kg of steam to evaporate a kilogram of water from the product instead of the 1.87 kg of steam required by machine B.

Machine B is turning out more finished product, not because it is more efficient as a dryer, but because it has less work to do.

Mechanical drying

The first part of many drying processes is to get rid of as much water as possible by mechanical means, so that the steam heated dryer shall have as little work to do as is possible. It is more economical to dry mechanically than with heat, but mechanical drying can be taken only to a certain stage.

Paper, for example, has a large percentage of its moisture extracted by suction through the wire on which the sheet is being formed, before passing to the dryer. Raw wool, after washing, is passed through squeeze rolls to extract some of the moisture. A laundry uses centrifugal water separators (hydro-extractors) before its steam heated drying plant and the housewife uses a spin dryer, which is exactly the same thing on a smaller scale, for the family washing.

If the mechanical drying plant is not operated efficiently and consistently, the steam heated dryers which follow will never produce good results. In the example of the two paper machines, a difference of only 2 % in the initial moisture content put on machine A the extra duty of evaporating another 0.013 kg/s. Because this machine uses 1.75 kg of steam to evaporate 1 kg of water, this would require an extra 0.023 kg/s of steam and increase the steam consumption of the machine by nearly 10 %.

This important factor of the efficiency of the mechanical drying plant is being stressed for two reasons. First for its own sake, because it is so important. Secondly because the inconsistent final drying which results from bad mechanical drying is so often laid at the door of the wretched steam traps.

Pipe dryers

Short pipe

The simplest form of dryer is a room or a space which is heated by pipes. Sometimes air is blown over the pipes by a fan, sometimes there is no forced air stream, for example in fur and skin drying.

The problems of steam trapping and air venting are greatly dependent on the exact layout of the piping.

Consider first the use of short lengths of piping with no forced air draught built up as shown in Figures 140, 141 and 142 in the form of vertical wall sections.

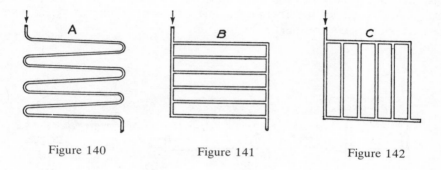

Figure 140   Figure 141   Figure 142

The important point to watch in Figure 140 is that the pipes are each given an adequate fall, so that condensate can gravitate naturally to the drain point. The peak load of condensate is not likely to be heavy and it is more than probable that such a heating unit will be working under steady conditions, maintaining an even temperature in the room. If there is no waterhammer, balanced pressure thermostatic or small float traps with automatic air release can be used. Inverted bucket traps will withstand waterhammer but for quick heating up an air vent in a by-pass may be required.

The heating units shown in Figures 141 and 142 are sometimes used but it is often difficult to get even heating due to steam by-passing some of the sections and air being trapped in them. The best that can be done is to mount the grid so that there is a natural fall towards the outlet and, if necessary, fit an air vent at the top right hand corner. Steam trapping is the same as for Figure 140.

If the room is not temperature controlled, it is as well to consider the use of a liquid expansion trap in Figure 140. This presupposes that the heating surface is adequate to allow for some waterlogging of the bottom part of the piping when the room is up to temperature. Such a trap will allow the Specific enthalpy of the condensate to do useful work before the condensate is discharged. This suggestion is not likely to be so helpful in Figures 141 and 142, owing to the arrangement of the pipes in parallel.

Long pipe

When drying rooms are heated by long lengths of pipe a different set of problems arises. Just because of the long lengths it is usual to find that the pipes have been laid without adequate fall towards the drain point. This causes waterhammer, a constant heavy water film in the bottom of the pipe, bad heat transfer, and so the use of an unnecessarily high pressure to get the required room temperature.

The layout should be modified, if at all possible, as shown in Figure 97 (page 103) where the problem is discussed in detail and appropriate trapping and air venting is recommended.

If the pipes are on or under the floor such an alteration may be difficult. Traps must then be chosen which will stand up to the inevitable waterhammer and the best choice is either the thermodynamic or inverted bucket types with a thermostatic air vent for quicker heating up.

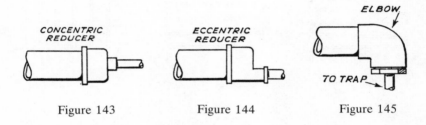

Figure 143   Figure 144   Figure 145

Since such heating pipes are often of larger diameter than the drain outlet to the trap – and it must be remembered that the trap should not be sized according to the diameter of the drain – it is important to see that the drain connection is never as shown in Figure 143 but always as shown in Figure 144 or 145. The use of a concentric reducer must obviously result in the bottom of the pipe being full of water and almost entirely out of action, so far as heat transfer is concerned. Fit the outlet as shown in Figure 144 or 145; get more useful surface, so that the steam pressure can be lowered for economy or more heat be made available to give greater room temperature.

Long pipe tentering machines

A special case of the long pipe dryer is the older type of tentering machine, once commonly used in the woollen and worsted industry, for fixing the dimensional stability of a length of cloth by drying it while holding it to a fixed width as it passes through the machine. Some of these are still working but many of them have been replaced by modern machines using heater batteries and forced air circulation which will be described in the next section.

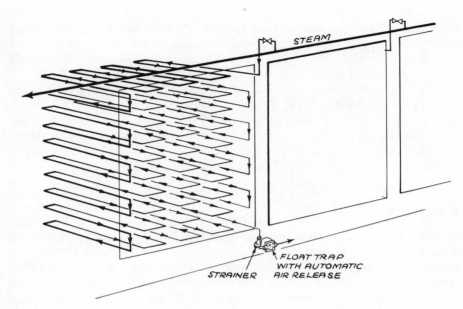

Figure 146

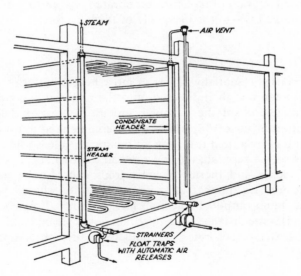

Figure 147

Figures 146 and 147 show two methods of arranging the pipe coils. In Figure 146 each bay is heated by a continuous coil of 25 mm (1″) pipe. Each coil is fed by a steam header at the top of the machine and is drained by a single steam trap. For maximum heat output a float trap with automatic air release or an inverted bucket trap should be used. In the latter case, an air vent fitted in a by-pass around the trap will speed starting up from cold. The steam header should be drained and air vented.

In Figure 147 the pipe coil has been split up into a number of lengths running between vertical steam and condensate headers and each of these is drained by a float or inverted bucket trap. An air vent at the top of the condensate header will speed the removal of air on start-up.

Condensate from all these machines is best drained by gravity to a flash vessel and then pumped back to the feed tank. However, it is not always possible to find a use for all the flash steam, which can then present a problem. In those cases where maximum heat output is not required, this has been successfully overcome by using bimetallic traps which discharge condensate below saturation temperature, waterlogging part of the pipe coil in the process.

Hot air dryers

Hot air is widely used for drying many different materials. The air has to perform two main functions – to heat up the material and moisture until the latter is evaporated and then to carry away the water vapour from the surface of the material. In many cases it would be extremely wasteful to discharge the air from the dryer after only one pass across the material and so some of the air is recirculated to allow it to pick up more moisture. In this way the steam consumption per kilogram of moisture evaporated is kept to a minimum as hot air is only discharged when it is incapable of further effective drying.

Heater batteries

Hot air dryers consist essentially of one or more heater batteries through which air is forced by a fan and then directed onto the material being dried.

A general discussion on the draining and air venting of heater batteries appears in Chapter 6 (page 108) where it is recommended that individual trapping of each battery by a float trap with automatic air release should be the first choice together with a separate thermostatic air vent when the design calls for this. Inverted bucket and thermodynamic traps can also be used. Where a battery is made up of a number of sections, these too should be individually trapped for maximum output. If the trap has to be fitted outside the machine casing, so that it is some distance from the drain point, steam locking is likely and a float trap with steam lock release should be used with a separate air vent fitted in parallel.

Ducted air tentering machines

In the previous section we said that modern tentering machines used hot air from heater batteries instead of pipe coils and this air is forced by fans through ducting so that it contacts the cloth in the most effective way for heating it and carrying off the moisture which is evaporated.

Often each bay has a number of small heater batteries fed with steam from a vertical header which should be trapped so that condensate, particularly when starting up, does not drain into the bottom battery and reduce its output.

Ideally, for maximum performance, each battery should be individually trapped, but in practice, for reasons of space and easy access for maintenance, this is not often done. Satisfactory results are obtained when the batteries are connected in small groups to vertical condensate headers from which pipes lead to the traps, conveniently grouped together in an accessible position. Float traps with steam lock releases each having a thermostatic air vent fitted in a by-pass are likely to give the best results. Inverted bucket traps are often used satisfactorily, however. It can be an advantage to remove air from the heater batteries by fitting an automatic air vent at the top corner furthest from the steam inlet.

Stenters

Stentering of woven cloth made from cotton or artificial fibres is the equivalent of tentering in the woollen industry although the machines used are quite different in layout. The cloth is held to a fixed width and hot air from heater batteries is blown on to it. Steam trapping and air venting of the batteries is done as before.

Wool dryers

Hot air dryers are also used for drying wool after scouring and dyeing. In some machines the wool passes through on a conveyor and hot air blows through it. In others, the wool is rotated or tumbled in perforated drums through which the hot air is forced but in all cases a heater battery of some sort is used. The recommendations for air and condensate removal are unchanged.

Laundry tumblers

The laundry tumbler is a hot air dryer in which the damp goods are rotated in a perforated basket through which hot air from a heater battery is blown. The first choice for draining the heater battery is, once again, a float trap with automatic air release.

Spray dryers

As an alternative to film drying, which is dealt with in the next section, liquid and semi-liquid materials such as milk and many chemicals are dried into powder by spray drying. In this process the liquid is sprayed in the form of small globules into a chamber through which hot air from a heater battery is passing. Drying is rapid because of the large surface area which the many small globules bring into contact with the hot air and the process can be completed before the material has risen to too high a temperature – a very important advantage in the case of some materials.

Here again the points which have already been made about trapping and air venting heater batteries apply.

In most spray dryers the batteries are made up of a number of sections and there will be a very big difference in condensing rate between the first section which is receiving cold air and the last. Because of lack of space, there is sometimes a temptation to group the various sections to a single trap but this is asking for trouble. Individual trapping is the way to get maximum output from the dryer and air venting also needs careful attention.

It is often possible to collect the flash steam from the traps draining the main batteries and use it at low pressure in additional batteries to preheat the air entering the dryer (see also Chapter 5).

Cylinder dryers

Much drying is done by passing the wet material or liquid over steam heated rotating cylinders. The finished material may be run off in long lengths, for example paper or textile; or may be scraped off the face of the cylinder by a fixed blade, for example milk powder or yeast product. Although this method of drying is in use in many industries and they each have their own particular detail differences the fundamental principles are the same.

In all cases condensate and air have to be removed from a heat transfer surface which is revolving and they can only be taken out through the centre of the bearing in which the cylinder is rotating. Careful attention to draining and air venting cylinder dryers should improve some or all of these common faults – slow heating up from cold, uneven drying, excessive steam consumption, excessive driving power consumption and wastage of finished product.

Film dryers

Figure 148 shows a typical twin cylinder dryer used for making milk powder. Liquid milk is fed into the trough-like space at the top between the two steam

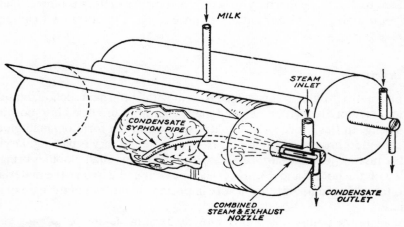

Figure 148

heated cylinders. A film of it is carried round under each cylinder, drying on the way, and is scraped off by a fixed 'doctor' blade high up on the outside. Steam is fed into each cylinder through one trunnion and condensate is taken away sometimes through the same trunnion or sometimes through the opposite one. Condensate must be lifted up from the bottom of the cylinder, where it collects, to the trunnion. In cylinder machines designed for drying liquids, it is usual to have a syphon pipe from the cylinder bottom to the trunnion; in this case the steam pressure in the cylinder lifts the condensate. The other method of raising the condensate is mechanically by an internal bucket or scoop. The illustration shows a film dryer with a combined inlet and outlet trunnion (or 'nozzle') and a syphon pipe.

Certain of these machines have a very considerable steam consumption. It is important to see that the steam feed pipes and the trunnion connections are adequate to pass sufficient steam to meet the starting up demand without undue pressure drop.

When steam is first turned on to a cylinder there will be a cylinder-full of air to be displaced. Unless this is discharged quickly, the air will mix with the incoming steam, reduce the steam temperature and form the typical air insulating film.

It is not uncommon to find damp spots in the film of dried material on the cylinder, particularly towards the edges. This must be due to uneven heat transference through the cylinder walls. The only condition which can vary between one part of the steam space and another sufficient to cause this uneven heat transference, is the thickness of the air and water films. It is, in fact, found that air venting the cylinder will get rid of this trouble.

The syphon drain pipe cannot come right down to the cylinder wall, but it is important that it should be as close as possible. Whenever the end of the syphon pipe is uncovered, as it must be at intervals, steam will enter the pipe and will, unless special provision is made, lock the steam trap. No more condensate will be discharged by the trap because it cannot get up the syphon pipe until the steam is condensed. Since the pipe is surrounded by steam, condensation will be very slow, and steam locking a serious problem.

It used to be common practice to fit one steam trap to drain both cylinders of a film dryer. Since either syphon pipe may be uncovered at any time and the connecting pipe from the trunnions to the trap must be of a considerable length, troubles due to steam locking are aggravated. The load on each cylinder is not likely to be exactly the same at all times, so the one trap arrangement produces the additional faults of group trapping.

It has been shown how important it is that the bottom of the syphon pipe should be kept covered as a help to prevent steam locking. It must be remembered that a steam trap having a large capacity will have to be used in order to cope with the starting load.

If therefore a trap with an intermittent discharge action is used, it will be a large trap delivering a considerable quantity of water at each blast. But such a trap is exactly the type which is most likely to cause the bottom of the syphon pipe to be uncovered. A trap which discharges condensate in a continuous stream is greatly to be preferred for this job. It is important that the pipe from the trunnion to the trap should be kept short. This calls for a comparatively light trap so that it can be fitted on the piping. There must be some steam lock release in the trap – this is most important. The trap must handle a heavy starting load and yet be equally efficient on the much smaller running load. The only type which answers to this specification is the float trap with internal steam lock release.

The necessity of air venting each cylinder has been shown, but it is no easy matter to decide the best place to fit the air vent. Figure 149 shows an arrangement which has in practice proved very successful.

A balanced pressure thermostatic air vent and collector pipe are connected in at the top of the exhaust nozzle. Most of the air present in the cylinder on starting up will be driven out up the syphon pipe to the vent. The air which remains will diffuse through the steam, but since the steam flow will be outwards towards the cylinder walls, the air will tend to collect here. The syphon pipe is taking water away from the walls, so there will be a general drift towards the pipe. The air will find itself gradually working outwards to the walls and then along the wall face to the outlet pipe and the vent.

Attempts are often made to lift the condensate from drying cylinders directly into an overhead return main. This arrangement may, in some cases, operate satisfactorily when the machine is up to temperature, but on starting up from cold there will, for some time, be insufficient pressure in the cylinder to overcome the lift, and the quick removal of air will be impossible. Condensate will, therefore, build up in the cylinder and before long pour out of the air vents, taking the path of least resistance. It is far better to run the condensate by gravity to a receiver and pump it up into the return as described in Chapter 3 (page 69). This will allow the cylinders to come up to temperature much more quickly.

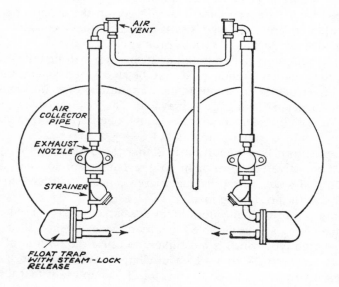

Figure 149

Paper making machines

A paper making machine consists of a number of steam heated cylinders over which a continuous length of wet paper stuff passes, gradually becoming dryer until the finished product is reeled off at the dry end of the machine. The number of cylinders may vary from half a dozen on some old machines up to 170 or more.

It is common for heat to be applied in stages to the material, a low heat at the wet end, increasing towards the dry end, although the last few cylinders sometimes run at a lower temperature to assist reeling. The general design of a cylinder in a paper making machine is often no different from the cylinder of a film dryer and condensate and air are removed through a syphon pipe which is either fixed, or in the case of high speed machines, rotates with the cylinder. Bucket water lifters are now only found in some old slow speed machines which are used for making special papers.

When a drying cylinder is rotating slowly steam condensing on the inside surface runs down to form a puddle at the lowest point. As the speed increases the puddle is first of all displaced in the direction of rotation, due to friction between the condensate and the cylinder, and then a thick layer of water is carried up towards the top of the cylinder until gravity causes it to break away and cascade back to the bottom. Finally, at even higher speeds, the centrifugal force overcomes gravity and a complete layer of condensate rotates with the cylinder. This is called rimming. The best way of handling the condensate and air will depend on the cylinder speed since this determines the behaviour of the condensate inside the cylinder.

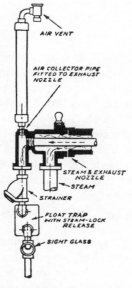

Figure 150

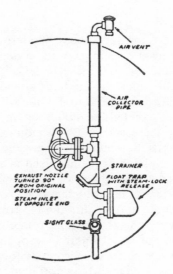

Figure 151

Let us first consider a machine running with a normal condensate puddle in the bottom of the cylinders. This corresponds to the condition in the cylinders of a film dryer and steam locking can take place in the syphon pipe. This calls for the fitting of a float trap with steam lock release together with an air vent on an air collector pipe tapped into the top of the exhaust nozzle. The trap should be protected by a strainer and followed by a sight glass. Figures 150 and 151 show two methods by which these arrangements can be carried out on different styles of exhaust nozzles.

By trapping individual cylinders in this way, the pressure in each can be adjusted independently of the others so that the required temperature gradient can readily be obtained along the machine. Group trapping a number of cylinders to a single steam trap is particularly unfortunate. As the paper is getting progressively drier in its passage through the machine, it is inevitable that each cylinder is less heavily loaded than the one before it. Group trapping, for this reason alone, will make it difficult for the more heavily loaded cylinders to discharge condensate to the trap. Added to this is the fact that the pressure at the outlet of a cylinder may at any moment be below or above that at the outlets of neighbouring cylinders because of individual setting of the steam inlet valves. The highest pressure cylinder will get steam to the trap first and so steam lock it.

Correct individual trapping and air venting of each cylinder in place of group trapping and no air venting has been proved by actual test to give such improvements as these:

18 cylinder machine – steam consumption down 20 % and also machine speed
up from 2.4 to 3.25 m/s and driving power consumption
down 20 % (due to elimination of water in cylinders)
47 cylinder machine – steam consumption down 25 %
16 cylinder machine – steam consumption down 12 %; driving power down
3.7 kW

Today however, many modern machines operate at speeds which cause cascading and rimming of the condensate and different methods must be used to drain and air vent the cylinders. It is impossible to set a precise figure to the speed at which the methods already described cease to be efficient but this is probably around 3.8 to 4.3 m/s with a 1.5 metre cylinder.

When condensate builds up in high speed cylinders the driving power is greatly increased and a stationary syphon pipe is subjected to very severe stresses as the water moves past the end of it. This has led to the development of rotary syphons which are fixed inside the cylinder and go around with it. Two opposed syphon pipes are commonly used and these form a unit which is easily supported by the cylinder walls. A special rotary joint is then used to lead the condensate and air through the trunnion.

However, as the syphons rotate their ends are likely to become uncovered by condensate, and if a normal trapping system were used very severe steam locking would occur. In practice it is found that the cylinders can only be drained properly if steam is blown straight through, carrying the condensate with it. This

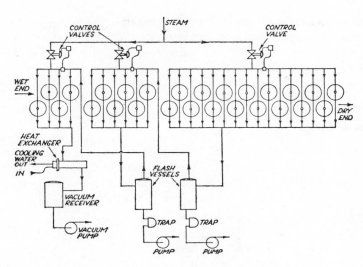

Figure 152

would obviously be very wasteful unless some way was found to use the surplus steam and this has led to the development of various stage or cascade systems, one of which is shown in Figure 152.

With these, live steam and condensate from a group of cylinders at the dry end of the machine, where steam pressure is highest, are taken to a flash vessel which separates the steam from the condensate. The former, at reduced pressure, is taken to the next group of cylinders while the condensate is drained by a float trap or level control and pumped back to the boiler for re-use. At the second stage the process is repeated and finally steam and condensate from the wet end cylinders, probably under vacuum, are passed through a heat exchanger to condense the steam and the condensate then goes to a receiver and vacuum pump. Live steam can be fed to any of the stages through pressure controllers to maintain steady stage pressures.

The number and arrangement of stages varies depending on the paper being dried and in some systems the flash steam from a stage is re-injected into that stage by steam injectors fed with high pressure steam. Quite sophisticated control equipment is normally used to maintain the correct drying rate from all the stages.

Even with a stage system, however, there is always more heat available from the steam blown through the cylinders than the machine itself can use. Some of the flash steam from intermediate stages is often used to supply roof and hood heaters. The former are used to prevent vapour condensing on cold roof surfaces above a paper machine and dripping onto the paper. Hood heaters form part of the drying system by heating up air and vapour given up by the paper as it is dried so that it can be blown back onto the paper surface to help evaporate more moisture.

Cooling water from the heat exchanger in the drain from the wet end cylinders is used for such purposes as stock preparation and wire washing. But when all possible uses for waste heat have been found it may still be necessary to discharge some unused. This is a price that has to be paid so as to carry out the drying process satisfactorily.

Paper calendering

A machine as shown in Figure 153 is used for calendering paper. The cylinders or 'bowls' are of small diameter and use high pressure, about 1100 kPa, steam. They are not so much for drying as for finishing the paper surface. The steam consumption is small, because temperature and not quantity of heat is the main consideration.

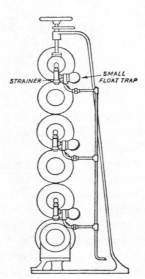

Figure 153

In the illustration the machine is shown with a small float trap with automatic air release draining each cylinder. If individual draining is adopted, the trap chosen must be very small, because there is so little space available. The smallest trap – a balanced pressure thermostatic type – is not put forward because of the pressure and the very low steam consumption. Such a trap would work well enough, but it is doubtful whether the element would stand up for a reasonable period. A small float or inverted bucket trap or a thermodynamic trap are the only other types which will fit in. Similarly there is no room to fit a separate air vent. Fortunately the quantity of air to be discharged from each cylinder is small. If these machines are drained by a single trap at the bottom of a common condensate header there is a likelihood of steam locking at the trap. Since the air from all the cylinders has to pass through the one trap it is desirable to fit a separate thermostatic air vent at the top of the common header. Of the two methods, individual draining appears to give the better results.

Corrugating machines

Corrugated board, in either single or double thickness, is widely used as a packing material. The corrugating machine takes in a continuous length of board, pre-conditions it with a steam spray, corrugates it, glues a plain board to either side of the corrugated sheet and finally dries the finished product. It comprises a number of steam heated cylinders, spray nozzles and steam chests on which the final drying is done.

The cylinders or rolls vary in size but most corrugating rolls are about 350 mm in outside diameter with an internal diameter of about 230 mm and are drained by syphon pipes. The corrugating and press rolls of older, slow speed machines should be individually drained, and an inverted bucket trap is probably the best choice to stand up to the considerable vibration. Steam locking and air removal are not problems because of the small size of the steam space. The larger rolls of the glue machine should be drained by float traps with steam lock release and air vents should be fitted on air collector pipes in the manner already described.

The beds of the steam chests are best drained by float traps with automatic air releases.

In the case of modern, high speed, machines some of the rolls operate at speeds high enough to cause rimming of the condensate and these are usually fitted with some form of blow-through system similar to that already described under 'Paper making machines'. This means that there are considerable quantities of surplus steam for which some use must be found. The live steam supplied to the machine is usually at pressures of the order of 1000 to 1400 kPa and the surplus steam can be at 1000 kPa and may amount to 0.125 kg/s. Fortunately this steam can be used in the pre-heating and pre-conditioning rolls, the steam sprays and the beds of the steam chests.

Finally, for satisfactory performance, the steam supply to a corrugating machine should be well drained as should the feeds to the various steam sprays which will otherwise soak the board with water instead of moisten it with steam.

Textile sizing machines

Figure 154 shows a two-cylinder Tape Frame or Slasher once universally used in the textile industry for drying sized material but now being replaced by faster multi-cylinder machines of the type shown in Figure 155. The resemblance to a paper making machine is obvious and the method of draining and air venting is similar in principle.

Multi-cylinder sizers are used for silk and artificial fibres as well as cotton and jute and, depending on the material, steam pressures in the cylinders can vary from below atmospheric up to around 420 kPa. Like a paper machine there may also have to be a temperature gradient along the sizer and when all these variations are coupled to a demand for increasing output the need for efficient individual draining and air venting of the cylinders becomes obvious.

Considering Figure 155 in detail, it will be seen that in this case the cylinders are fed from a steam header at low level which is drained by a float trap. With

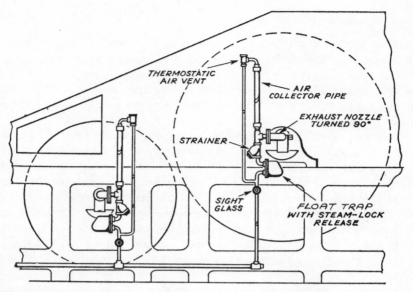

Figure 154

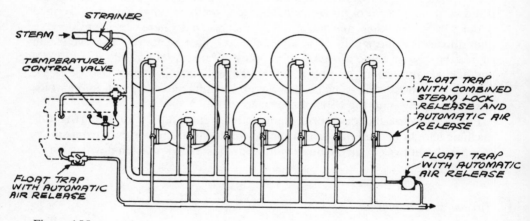

Figure 155

this arrangement the branch pipes to the cylinders naturally come off the top of the header but they should still do this even if the header is above the cylinders, so that the latter are fed with dry steam. Inverted bucket or thermodynamic traps can be used in place of the float trap if desired.

The first steam requirement is for heating the size bath. This may be done either by open injection through a perforated sparge pipe (which dilutes the size) or by closed coil. In some cases, particularly where a lot of size is used, it is mixed and heated in steam jacketed or coil heated kettles separate from the machines and is then circulated to a number of size baths through a ring main by means of a pump. Shell and tube heat exchangers are also used.

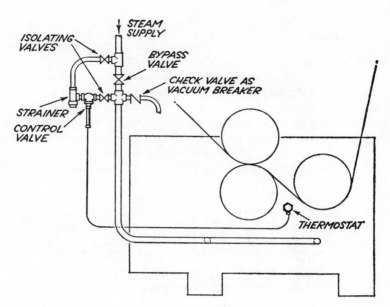

Figure 156

In all cases, some form of temperature regulator will be needed to hold the size at the correct temperature for the mixture being used. Figure 155 shows a coil heated size bath fitted with a temperature regulator and drained by a float trap with automatic air release. A temperature regulator will also be needed where direct steam injection is used as shown in Figure 156. Jacketed size kettles are similar to the jacketed pans described in Chapter 7 (page 118) and heat exchangers are like the heating calorifiers dealt with in Chapter 6 (page 98).

After the branch to the size bath there are steam feeds to the cylinders which may vary in number, being usually five, seven or nine. A common cylinder diameter is 550 mm, and 750 mm cylinders are also used.

Condensate and air are discharged from each cylinder through a syphon pipe to a float trap with both steam lock release and automatic air release. The comparatively small combined inlet and outlet nozzles are unable to support the weight of separate air vents fitted to air collector pipes.

Experience has shown that better air removal with increased output can be obtained if the air vents are connected directly into the end of the cylinders with an elbow screwed to each outlet connection and pointing at the cylinder end. The air vent, therefore, rotates with the cylinder and should it occasionally discharge a small spit of water, this will be evaporated immediately by the hot cylinder and do no harm.

Where a machine is constantly running with a sub-atmospheric pressure in the cylinders because of the low temperatures required, the air vents are dispensed with. Under these conditions the vacuum breakers on the cylinder ends will open periodically to allow air into the cylinders and the resulting mixture of steam and air will produce the necessary low temperature.

Textile multi-cylinder dryers

Apart from sizing, multi-cylinder dryers are also used in the textile industry for drying continuous lengths of cloth after wet processing. Machines are in use with the cylinders arranged both vertically and horizontally, although the latter are being replaced by modern high speed machines consisting of a number of vertical stacks of 'cans'.

Figures 157 and 158 show the traditional machines, no longer made, which use the hollow cast iron frames on each side as steam and condensate headers. Steam pressure is a maximum of 70 kPa and condensate is removed by rotating buckets. The cylinders are group trapped and no provision is made for air venting.

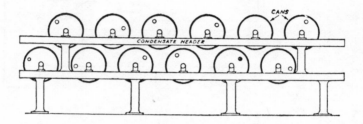

Figure 157

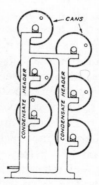

Figure 158

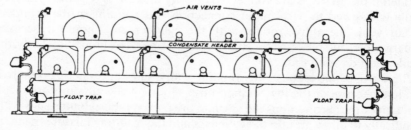

Figure 159

The greatest improvement in output can be obtained in those cases where it is possible to make structural alterations, such as fitting blanking pads between each dollhead and the frame, so that the cylinders can be individually drained and air vented, using a small float or inverted bucket trap. A compromise arrangement is shown in Figure 159. Each end of the two horizontal frame members on the condensate side of the machine is drained by a float trap with automatic air release fitted close up to prevent steam locking. In addition air vents are fitted as shown at intervals along these frame members. The ends of the steam inlet headers should also be drained and air vented so that steam reaches the cans as quickly as possible when starting up from cold.

It is on record that the fitting of four automatic air vents to the common condensate header of a horizontal drying machine reduced the heating up time from 90 minutes to 10. The temperature difference between the inlet and exhaust ends of the cans were reduced from 17 °C to 3 °C.

The same principles of trapping and air venting can be applied to the older vertical dryers with cast iron frames (Figure 160).

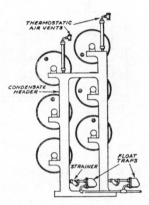

Figure 160

Modern vertical machines consist of a number of separate stacks of cans called stations and use fabricated frame members to support the cans. Steam is fed either into the frame member on one side, usually through a reducing valve so that the temperature of each station can be separately controlled, or to each cylinder individually, and condensate is removed by a syphon pipe to the opposite trunnion. Combined nozzles are also used in which case the steam feed and condensate piping will be on the same side of the machine.

In some cases the cylinders in a station all drain into the vertical frame member to which a float trap with automatic air vent should be fitted. An air vent should also be fitted to the top of each frame. The best arrangement is where each cylinder is drained individually by a float trap incorporating both steam lock release and automatic air release (see Figure 161). Inverted bucket traps are also used. Each vertical steam header should also be trapped so that dry steam is fed to the cans.

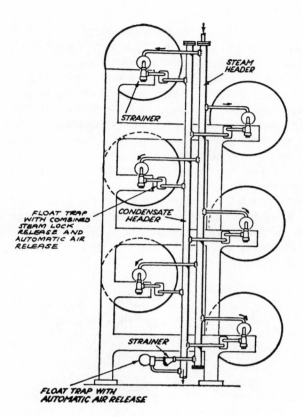

STEAM HEADER

STRAINER

FLOAT TRAP WITH COMBINED STEAM LOCK RELEASE AND AUTOMATIC AIR RELEASE

CONDENSATE HEADER

STRAINER

Figure 161

FLOAT TRAP WITH AUTOMATIC AIR RELEASE

Steam pressures in modern vertical dryers vary considerably, up to 420 kPa being common, but the need for increased production is causing even higher pressures to be used, coupled with high cylinder speeds. Indeed the latter are beginning to produce the condensate rimming problems inside the cylinders which have already been described under Paper making machines, and similar means must be employed to get the condensate out of the cylinder.

Multi-cylinder dryers can take up a lot of floor space and this has led to the development of more compact machines using a combination of contact drying by cylinders and hot air from heater batteries. In some machines the hot air blows through jets arranged radially around the cylinders so that the material is forced into firmer contact with the cylinder face so improving heat transference. Float traps with inbuilt steam lock release and automatic air vent are best for draining the cylinders, with a similar trap but without steam lock release on each heater battery.

In a machine of this type the cylinders normally work at a maximum pressure of 420 kPa, whereas the heater batteries may be fed with steam at 1400 kPa. There should, therefore, be scope for recovering flash steam from the traps draining the heater batteries and using it in the cylinders, so saving some live steam.

Contact dryers

The cylinder dryers already considered are, of course, contact dryers – that is, the material to be dried is brought into direct contact with a steam heated surface – but they have been treated as a separate item because of their importance. Besides contact dryers of the cylinder type, there are such items of plant as calenders, presses and rotary dryers.

Calenders

Calenders or ironers such as are used in a laundry are unlike the paper calendering machines already considered. Although they impart a finish to the material passing through, their main use of steam is for drying. They have cylinders, but in many cases these are unheated and it is the bed of the machine that supplies the heat for evaporating the moisture from the goods being dried. Where the roll is heated this is primarily to dry the clothing which picks up moisture from the wet material. The tendency is for a given size of machine to be called on for more and more output, so maximum heat transfer through the beds is vital.

Ironers vary very greatly in design and each one has to be considered individually from the standpoint of trapping and air venting. Beds may be made from cast iron or fabricated from steel plate. With the latter, even heating is most important otherwise the bed may distort and damage the goods passing through the machine. In these cases proper condensate and air removal are vital.

For a start the steam supply header should be drained and the best performance will be obtained if a steam dryer is fitted. This can be drained with a float or inverted bucket trap protected by a strainer.

Then each bed section of a multi-roll machine must be drained individually. Any attempt at group trapping will reduce the output of the machine and cause unsatisfactory drying. The amount of space under modern machines is very restricted and the whole ironer is cased in, so the tendency is to group the traps together at one end where they are accessible for maintenance. This inevitably means long connecting pipes between the drain outlets on the beds and the traps with the danger of steam locking. The best trap to use is a float trap incorporating both steam lock release and automatic air vent. Thermodynamic traps are also used successfully but they should be fitted close up to the drain point. Since their correct working depends on the loss of heat from the cap of the trap, care should be taken when they are fitted under fully enclosed machines where the ambient temperature can be very high. If heated airing gaps are used, they too should be individually trapped.

Depending on the internal shape of the bed, air vents may be needed at the horns to remove all the air which fills the bed on starting up from cold (see also Chapter 4, page 81).

If the rolls are heated both air and condensate must be removed from them. The duty of a calender roll is not high enough to justify the use of a float trap with steam lock release and separate air vent such as would be used on a paper

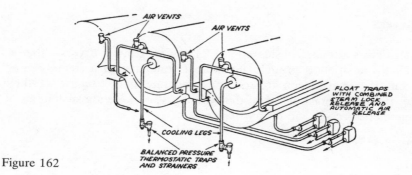

Figure 162

machine cylinder. The first choice is a balanced pressure trap and strainer fitted on a cooling leg about 1 metre long which will clear the air out of the roll quickly when starting up. Thermodynamic traps are also used, fitted close to the trunnion.

Figure 162 shows a typical arrangement on a three roll ironer with airing gaps.

Presses

A steam heated press may be used to perform a combined drying and finishing operation, as in a laundry, or it may be used to mould, squeeze or heat treat a substance, as in plastics manufacture. We are considering here the first type only.

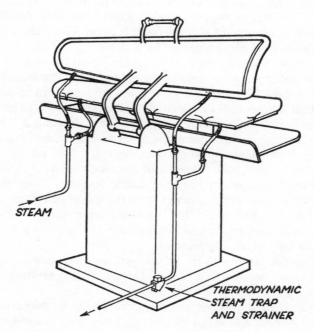

Figure 163

Figure 163 shows a typical laundry press. The fixed bottom section is heated as is also the top movable head. The steam consumption is low; air tends to find its way to the drain outlet, because the steam space is small. Theoretically it is better to drain both halves separately, because of the restriction put on the flow of condensate from the top section by the moving pipe arrangement. In practice this is sometimes done, but it is more usual to find one trap doing the job of draining and air venting the whole machine. Thermodynamic traps have proved very satisfactory and their small size makes them easy to install. Small float, balanced pressure or inverted bucket traps can also be used. The practice of draining more than one press to a trap is not recommended.

In the case of twin presses, where two tables are rotated so that each comes in turn under a single head, the two tables are drained by one trap and the head by another. If one trap is used for the whole press group trapping troubles will occur and drying will be unsatisfactory.

Rotary dryers

A particular form of steam heated rotary machine used for the contact drying of granular materials is shown in Figure 164. The heating element is a nest of tubes which rotate on a former, and in rotating scoop up the material to be dried so that it falls over the hot tubes. Steam passes along the tubes and condensate flows back to a sump at the inlet end. There it is picked up by a series of buckets and flows back through the trunnion round the central inlet steam pipe to the condensate outlet.

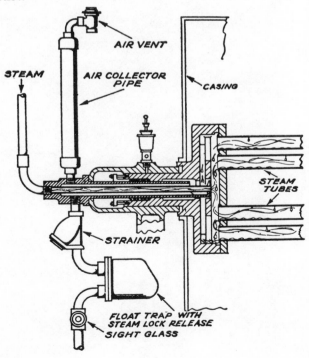

Figure 164

The machine is difficult to air vent efficiently, but air venting is most certainly required. An automatic balanced pressure thermostatic air vent fitted on a collector pipe as shown is the best, and indeed the only, solution. Since steam from the inlet can by-pass round the bucket lifter and close the trap, steam locking is a real danger. Steam consumption is very heavy when the material is wet, but light when drying is nearly complete. A float trap with steam lock release, fitted as shown, is the best recommendation for the work.

Low temperature dryers

Some materials have to be dried slowly at low temperatures, often well below that of steam at atmospheric pressure, otherwise they are damaged. An example is the drying of animal skins, used in the manufacture of leather goods, which are traditionally dried in stoves by hot air either from a steam coil on the floor or a heater battery.

A modern development for speeding up this process is a contact dryer which takes the form of a platen press of special design. The two platens between which the skins are held are heated by hot water while a vacuum is applied to speed up the removal of moisture.

The hot water is produced in a heat exchanger, using steam as the heating medium, and is circulated through the platens by a pump. The temperature of the water can be readily controlled by a thermostat operating a control valve on the steam supply. The heat exchanger is similar to the heating calorifier described in Chapter 6 (page 98) and is trapped and air vented in the same way.

9 Process treatment by steam

Steam heat is applied to many materials to change their nature or to facilitate chemical reaction or manipulation. This treatment is carried out in a variety of different plants often peculiar to one industry.

Heating for manipulation

Hot plates

Under the heading of steam heated plant used to assist the handling of a material come hot plates of one type or another. Whether the material is toffee or rubber, the hot plate on which it is rolled or spread has the same characteristics so far as draining and air venting is concerned.

Figure 165 shows one common but unsatisfactory method of feeding steam to a hot table. It will be seen that condensate and air from any section has to pass through each succeeding section before reaching the trap. This must inevitably result in slow heating up and a reduced temperature on the end sections.

Figure 166 shows a better method of steam supply, draining and air venting. The sections of the table are in parallel, but they are group trapped.

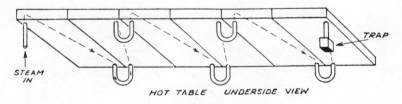

Figure 165

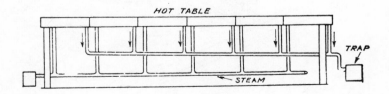

Figure 166

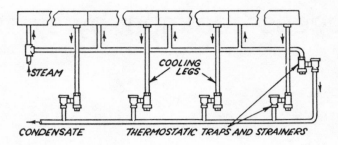

Figure 167

Figure 167 shows the best method and the one which will give the highest surface temperatures and quickest heating up.

As steam consumption is light, and pressures generally are low, balanced pressure thermostatic traps are very suitable; they can be fitted as shown. Alternatively thermodynamic, inverted bucket or float traps may be used but the first two will not be so successful in giving a quick discharge of air from the sections.

Wool combs

The steam circles of a wool comb are only a specialized type of hot plate to assist the manipulation of material. If the yarn is to come off the comb evenly it is important to achieve even heating of the circles and this is best done by using two traps. There is very little room available and Figure 168 shows how two small balanced pressure thermostatic traps can be fitted, one draining the large circle and the other the two smaller ones.

If only one trap is used, the three circles should be fed in parallel and the three outlets connected together and then to the trap.

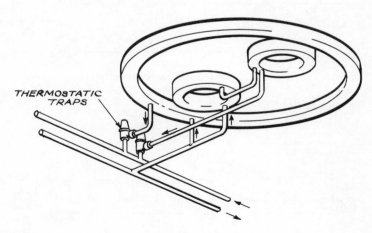

Figure 168

The practice of group trapping a number of combs to a single trap is not recommended because of the possibility of individual combs going cold, with consequent damage to the teeth unless the machine is shut down before the grease in the wool gets too thick for combing.

As an alternative to balanced pressure traps, thermodynamic traps have been satisfactorily used on wool combs.

Mélangeurs and *conches*

The manipulation of chocolate and its raw materials requires the application of carefully controlled heat at all stages of manufacture. In a *mélangeur* the grinding and mixing in of cocoa and sugar is carried out, the bed of the machine being heated by a steam coil. In a *conche* the cocoa, sugar and butter are blended intimately together and the machine is heated with hot water. The water may be supplied by a circulation system from a steam heated, temperature controlled calorifier; or there may be a steam coil in the water in the machine; or steam may be injected direct into the water in the machine.

In the latter case the device shown in Figure 93 (page 101) can be used. This combines an injection nozzle and a liquid expansion thermostat to throttle the steam supply and maintain a constant water temperature.

The problem of draining and air venting the steam coil of either a *mélangeur* or a *conche* is similar. Temperature and load conditions are very steady and the coil is only a simple, low pressure radiator. A small balanced pressure thermostatic trap, fitted one metre from the coil outlet, is all that is necessary.

Tracer lines

When viscous liquids, such as heavy fuel oils and certain chemicals, have to be pumped along a main, they must first be heated and then kept warm until they reach the point at which they are used. This is commonly done by running a small bore tracer pipe parallel to the main and feeding it with steam. Some times the tracer is in contact with the main and at others it is spaced from it but the two are enclosed in the same lagging to minimise heat losses.

Tracer lines should fall in the direction of steam flow and should not exceed 18 m in length for 10 mm ($^3/_8''$) pipe or 45 m for larger sizes. Each length should be drained by a steam trap. If the main is flanged, the tracer has to be looped to clear the flanges and it is important to arrange these loops so that condensate can

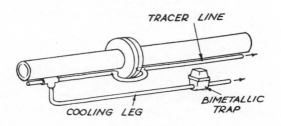

Figure 169

not collect in them, otherwise they must be drained. Where the tracer is at the side of the main, there is no problem, but if it is at the bottom the loops should always be horizontal and not dip down under the flange (see Figure 169).

Because the duty of a tracer line is normally light it is often permissible to use a bimetallic trap fitted close to the drain point so that condensate is held back in the tracer until some of the Specific enthalpy of water has been used. This has the added advantage that the amount of flash steam at the trap outlet is considerably reduced, which may be an important factor on a large site where the traps must discharge to atmosphere. If full heat output is required, fit the bimetallic trap on an unlagged cooling leg about 2 m long.

Thermodynamic or balanced pressure traps with steel bodies can be used as alternatives to the bimetallic type. Thermodynamic traps should be sized carefully in view of the small quantity of condensate produced by the average tracer. All these traps, besides being small in size and easy to install, can also be made to resist frost damage which can otherwise occur on exposed sites.

Jacketed pipes

Pipes carrying certain liquids are surrounded by a steam jacket to ensure even heating of the material so as to prevent any tendency to local cooling and possible solidification or chemical reaction.

Jacketed pipes are normally made in sections not exceeding 6 metres in length, and, ideally, each should be individually trapped. If this is not practicable, in moderate climates several lengths up to a maximum of 24 to 30 metres may be joined together and drained by a single trap. In those countries where very severe winters occur, the maximum length should not exceed 12 metres. Adjacent sections of the jacket should be connected at both top and bottom as shown in Figure 170 so that steam and condensate can flow freely and independently.

Trapping is similar to that of tracer lines and bimetallic, balanced pressure or thermodynamic traps can be used.

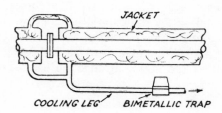

Figure 170

Fuel oil heating

Some fuel oils must be kept in heated storage tanks and be further heated before being fed to the oil burner. The trapping of steam coil heated storage tanks is dealt with in Chapters 7 and 10 (pages 128 and 177).

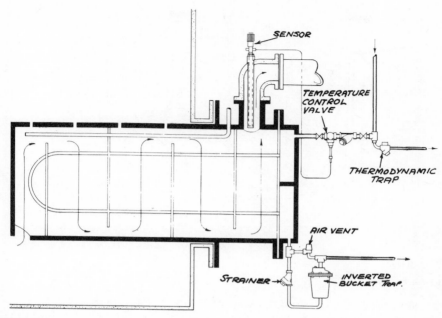

Figure 171

In many fuel oil installations, for reasons of economy, the bulk of the oil in the storage tank is kept at a fairly low temperature. The oil leaving the tank is then raised to pumping temperature by an outflow heater which is a shell and tube heat exchanger, similar to that shown in Figure 171, mounted in the wall of the tank at the oil outlet.

Outflow heaters are usually temperature controlled and work under continuous flow conditions, so that the first choice would normally be a float trap with automatic air release. But these heaters often work outdoors under very tough conditions and so an inverted bucket trap is probably a better choice, with an air vent fitted in parallel. The steam supply to the heater should be drained before the temperature control valve and a thermodynamic trap is suitable.

Line heaters are used to raise the oil up to burning temperature and are single or multi-stage heat exchangers. They should be treated in the same way as outflow heaters but, because they are normally fitted indoors, where freezing is not so likely, they can be drained by float traps with automatic air releases.

Inverted bucket traps with an air vent in parallel can also be used.

Heating for reaction

In the chemical and metal treatment industries steam heat is applied to vessels of many types, sizes and shapes to assist reaction. It is impossible to cover all the variations in use, neither is it necessary for our purpose, because the problems of draining and air venting are common to them all.

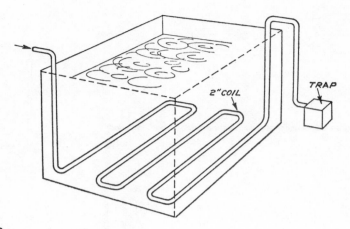

Figure 172

Vats and tanks

The commonest type of vessel in this class is the open top tank with a steam coil in the bottom, such as a plating vat or tar/liquor recovery tank. At one time it was common for steam coils to be badly designed, as shown in Figure 172. Because of the corrosive nature of the liquid being heated, it is probably impossible to have the outlet of the coil coming through the bottom or side of the tank. If, for example, a 50 mm (2″) coil of a certain length is necessary to provide the required amount of heat, it was not unusual to find this coil laid, as shown, flat on the floor and coming up full bore over the side to the steam trap. In practice this coil must be waterlogged for the greater part of its length most of the time, waterhammer will be about as bad as possible and the trap will be steam locked at regular intervals. Accurate temperature control of the liquid in the tank, if such is required, will be hopeless.

The points which need altering are as follows. There should be some fall, however slight, towards the point where the outlet pipe rises. If it is impossible to arrange this with a long continuous coil the layout should be changed to that shown in Figure 173. An inlet and an outlet header are arranged across each end of the tank and the heating pipes are run in a parallel manner between them. It is now much easier to have a fall from inlet to outlet while leaving the greater part of the tank free for the components being processed.

There must be a seal at the point where the outlet pipe rises to prevent steam from the coil getting to the steam trap and closing it off, thus holding back water in the coil. Figures 174, 175 and 176 show three ways of making this seal. In Figure 174 a simple loop has been made in the pipe. Figure 175 shows an arrangement of pipe fittings to serve the same purpose. Figure 176 shows a small diameter dip pipe, inside the main coil, pushed down as far as possible into the outlet bend. The third point which needs alteration concerns the rising pipe itself; this should be much smaller in diameter than the main coil. The smaller the rising pipe, the easier it will be for steam to force water up the pipe and

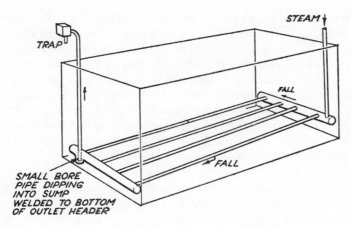

Figure 173

maintain an unbroken column. It follows that the loop in Figure 174 is not satisfactory unless the pipe diameter is reduced after it. The Figure 175 arrangement provides this reduced diameter in a convenient form. But it may be that fittings cannot be obtained in a metal which will withstand the corrosive action of the liquid. In such a case, the dip pipe method of Figure 176 is the best alternative, especially if this can be combined with the Figure 174 loop to receive the end of the dip pipe.

If reasonable heating of the liquid has been obtained in the past with, say, a 50 mm (2″) coil imperfectly drained, it stands to reason that better results can be obtained in the future with the same pipe if it is properly drained.

Assuming that these alterations have been made, the type of trap to be used on the outlet depends on the process. If it is desired to maintain the liquid at a

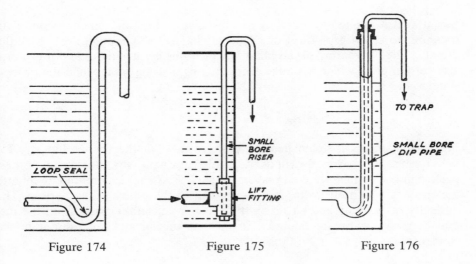

Figure 174   Figure 175   Figure 176

constant temperature and automatic control is provided on the steam inlet, a trap which discharges condensate at a steady rate and at steam temperature is likely to be best. A float trap with built in air release is needed. If there are large fluctuations in liquid temperature – due perhaps to batches of material being dumped in – and the liquid must regain its operating temperature quickly, then float, inverted bucket, thermodynamic or balanced pressure traps can all be used. The float trap should have an automatic air release and the inverted bucket and thermodynamic traps may need a separate air vent fitted in a by-pass. If an inverted bucket trap has to be installed at the top of the rising pipe, a check valve should be fitted close to the inlet to prevent loss of water-seal (see Chapter 3, page 69).

The thermodynamic trap is particularly useful where corrosive conditions exist because it is available made entirely from stainless steel.

If proper provision has not been made for getting condensate to the trap, there will be waterhammer and correct drainage will be impossible. Thermodynamic or inverted bucket traps will stand this abuse but it is far better to change the layout and eliminate the waterhammer.

Reaction vessels

Coil heated reaction vessels present problems of draining similar to those just discussed and the same careful attention must be paid to getting condensate up to the trap.

Jacketed reaction vessels should be drained and air vented on similar lines to the jacketed pans described in Chapter 7 (pages 120–2). Particular attention must be paid to the removal of air, which should be vented at a point remote from the steam entry to the jacket.

Heating for physical change

Steam heat is applied to a variety of substances, sometimes in conjuction with pressure, to effect a physical or chemical change. This section deals with the draining and air venting of the plant in which this is carried out and it includes also certain plant which is similar from the engineering rather than the process standpoint.

Open vulcanizers

Figure 177 shows a steam heated retort as used in the rubber industry for vulcanizing. A horizontal cylinder is loaded up with, say, hot water bottles, packed in trays which slide on perforated shelves. Steam is admitted direct into the space. Condensate forms and runs down to the outlet at the bottom. The difficulty of draining and air air venting such a vulcanizer arises from the fact that corrosive acids are liberated in the vulcanizing and are present in the condensate.

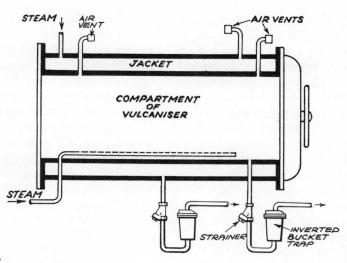

Figure 177

Any trap will rot away in time and the best choice is either an inverted bucket trap or a float trap with automatic air release the element of which is made from stainless steel.

Air venting of the steam space is an obvious advantage, as the air will tend to hang in pockets round the material. Thermostatic air vents are now available in corrosion resisting materials but the elements may need renewing periodically, especially if the corrosion is severe. However, this is a small price to pay for the improvement in the vulcanizing process resulting from their use. Several air vents may be needed, the number and position depending on the size of the chamber and the arrangement of the steam inlet.

Figure 177 shows the usual arrangement with steam fed in at the bottom through a perforated pipe. Most of the air will be forced upwards and the air vents should be at the top. If steam enters at the top of the chamber the air will be forced down towards the drain point and an air vent should be fitted in parallel with the trap.

In order to assist in the maintenance of a high temperature, the inner compartment of a vulcanizer is surrounded by a steam jacket.

The draining and air venting of this jacket is a separate and a simpler problem and float or inverted bucket traps can be used. The jacket should be air vented, as shown, by a balanced pressure thermostatic air vent.

The corrosive condensate from an open vulcanizer cannot be used as boiler feed, but Figure 8 (page 22) illustrates a method of saving some of its heat before it is run to waste.

Canning retorts (batch)

The retorts used for canning foods are very similar in construction to open vulcanizers, and they also bear a family resemblance to hospital sterilizers.

Canning retorts can be horizontal or vertical, rectangular or circular, and vary in capacity from just over 1 m^3 to more than 10 m^3. Unlike open vulcanizers and hospital sterilizers they are not jacketed and steam is usually brought in at the bottom and distributed over the area of the retort by perforated injection pipes.

Cans are packed in, the retort is closed up and steam is turned on. Condensation is very heavy and the pressure builds up only slowly. As in vulcanizers, the important thing is to get the correct temperature into all parts of the retort and to hold it for a certain length of time so that each can shall be cooked through to the centre. This is not easy because of the air pockets which can be left between the cans, and suggestions for overcoming this problem have already been made when discussing air venting of large steam spaces in Chapter 4 (page 83). In modern hospital sterilizers, where a similar problem arises, air is drawn out of the chamber by a vacuum pump. In canning retorts air is forced out of vents in the top by the steam pressure, which does not seem to be quite such a positive method.

When cooking and sterilization are complete the cans are often cooled by admitting cold water into the retort. This causes a rapid fall in the pressure acting on the outside of the cans and to prevent them from distorting, compressed air is often used to maintain the pressure in the retort while the cans are cooling. When the cans are cooled, pressure is released, the water is run out and the cans are removed.

In some retorts, depending on the nature of the product and the operating pressures and temperatures, the cycle times are very short and automatic control gear is used to open and close the various steam, compressed air, cooling water and air vent valves. However there are still many retorts using longer cycle times which are not equipped with automatic controllers and in these cases much better results will be obtained by fitting automatic air vents instead of manual cocks.

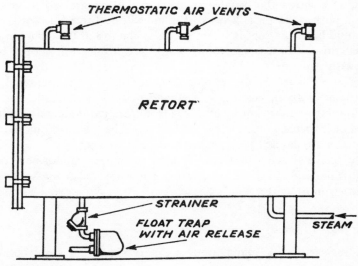

Figure 178

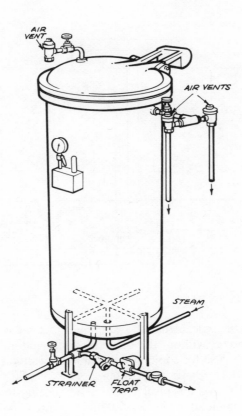

Figure 179

Figure 178 shows a horizontal canning retort complete with recommended draining and air venting arrangements. The trap chosen is a float trap with thermostatic air release fitted close to the outlet after a strainer. The air vents are of the balanced pressure thermostatic type.

Figure 179 shows similar equipment fitted to a vertical retort.

The complete and rapid removal of air from a large retort calls for special measures and the arrangement shown in Figure 80 (page 85) has been used very successfully. Steam is best fed into the top of the retort through one or more perforated pipes running the full length for even distribution. This forces the air downwards to special air outlets at the bottom, controlled by an automatic temperature control which acts like a large thermostatic air vent. The control valve can be set to remain open until all the air has been discharged. Even if steam is injected into the bottom of the retort, the same temperature control arrangement can be used at the top of the retort in place of separate air vents.

One final point to watch is the likelihood of grease and debris from the outside of the cans finding its way down with the condensate and choking the steam traps.

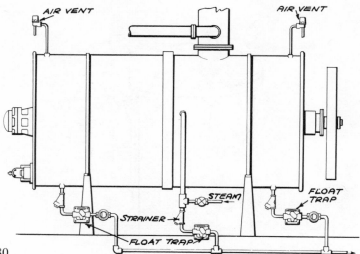

Figure 180

Digesters

By an extension of the vulcanizing and canning retort, we come to the digester. This is a process cooker without the direct steam injection, but with the steam jacket. Digesters are used for cooking waste animal products, and many of them have a rotating paddle to stir the contents. This paddle is sometimes steam heated. Figure 180 shows a typical layout. The starting load of condensate is heavy, and the running load, while considerable, is much less. Because the plant is generally of fair size, the volume of air which is present in the jacket when steam is first turned on presents quite a problem, as this air should be released as soon as possible. The trap chosen should be free from air binding troubles and should be fitted as close as possible to the outlet, so as to minimize steam locking. A float trap with thermostatic air release is perhaps the best choice. Two air vents are suggested as an aid to quick venting; the position of the air vents will, as usual, depend upon the position of the steam inlet, which, in digesters, may be either at the top, in the middle, or at the bottom. If a trap, as for example an inverted bucket trap, is used which will not discharge a lot of air, then an air vent should be fitted in a by-pass around the trap.

If the paddle is heated it should be drained by a float trap with steam lock release.

Rubber vulcanizing presses

The manufacture of certain rubber articles, for example tyres, calls for a simultaneous vulcanizing and moulding process. This is carried out in a steam heated press. One form of this is shown in Figure 181. There are two heated sections, the lower being fixed and the upper movable. Steam is taken to the movable part through flexible jointed pipes and condensate is led away through similar means.

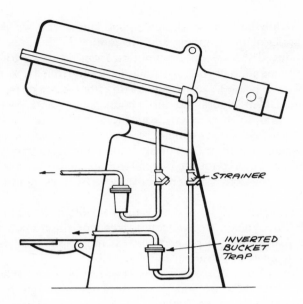

Figure 181

The heat requirements of each press are small, but the temperature requirements are very exacting. If any part of the rubber is not kept up to full temperature for the correct period, a soft cure will result. It is very common to find fully automatic time–temperature controllers fitted to these presses. There is no doubt that this is the best of all methods for getting the desired results. The removal of air and condensate is taken care of by a temperature control valve, which forms part of the equipment, and which serves the same purpose as an inbuilt thermostatic steam trap. Any change of temperature conditions in the steam space of the press is registered by the sensitive bulb, which immediately operates a relay and brings about an alteration of steam supply or condensate discharge which restores the correct temperature.

There are many rubber presses which are not equipped with time–temperature controls and these must be drained and air vented by more normal methods. The load of condensate is small, but it must be removed at steam temperature. The volume of air is not great, but any air film should be discouraged. Air will be discharged most readily from the drain point. A trap having a blast discharge is to be preferred. It is important that the trap should not air bind. The best trap to use for the job is the inverted bucket type but float or thermodynamic traps can also be fitted.

Multi-platen presses

Steam heated presses with a number of vertically moving platens are used for making certain rubber and plastic articles, for forming sheets of plaster board and for expressing cocoa butter, to name only a few applications. The importance of correct draining and air venting of these presses cannot be over-stressed, but the difficulties of arranging a satisfactory system are considerable. To show how much care can usefully be taken to design a good layout, it is worth mentioning that the re-designing of the trapping and air venting in the press section of a plastics works reduced the steam consumption from 52 to 28 tonnes a week, improved the product and cut the losses due to waste from 10 % to 4 %.

The platens of these presses are arranged with either series or parallel feed. In the series layout, steam enters the top platen, steam and condensate pass through flexible piping to the second, from there to the third and so on. It is inevitable that the lower platens should be less effective than the first one. In order to get adequate heat from the bottom platen it is necessary to use a steam pressure which is not required for the top platen. This in itself is wasteful. The air and water films in the lower platens must be a serious hindrance to heat transference.

Where series connection of the platens is unavoidable a robust blast discharge trap such as a thermodynamic or inverted bucket type should be used. Because all the air in the platens will be pushed towards the trap it is advisable to fit a separate automatic air vent as shown in Figure 182.

When the platens of these presses are arranged in parallel, steam is fed to a common header; branches are led to each platen through flexible pipes; condensate is discharged from each platen through flexible pipes to a common condensate header. These connecting pipes may take the form of flexible hoses or rigid lengths of pipe and swivel joints and this arrangement has its own particular troubles. If the steam and condensate headers are at the same height on either side of the press, the flexible pipes will loop and have water pockets. If it is possible, it is a good idea to have the steam header lifted and the condensate header lowered. This gives an easier and more natural flow. The steam header should be drained.

It will be noted that this parallel arrangement of platens may lead to group trapping troubles if a single trap is used to drain the condensate header. It is true

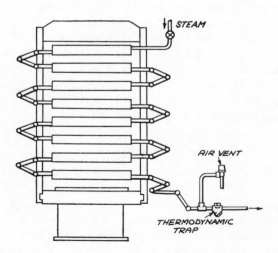

Figure 182

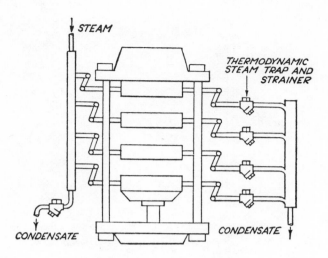

Figure 183

that all the platens come into operation together and there should be no difference in the pressure drop through each one. Whether it is due to the difference in static head between the platens or the steam locking of the trap on the condensate header, it is often found that the bottom platens do not heat up so well when this arrangement is used. Should such be the case, the individual trapping of platens should be considered. Figure 183 shows a layout using thermodynamic traps with inbuilt strainers draining each platen. Because a number of these traps may discharge simultaneously, it is important to size the condensate header generously and to use swept connections. This will prevent the back pressure building up sufficiently to reduce the dynamic effect and make the traps blow. In practice this layout has proved very successful, but it is not always possible to find room for the traps.

If one trap is to be used to drain the condensate header choose one with a blast discharge action such as the thermodynamic or inverted bucket types. An automatic air vent should be fitted to the top of the condensate header and a similar air vent can, often with advantage, be fitted in parallel with the trap.

Many presses of this type are water cooled after the initial steam heating operation is completed. The layout shown in Figure 183 can still be used, but the trap on the inlet header must be isolated while water is being admitted. This can be done if the water feed is arranged as shown in Figure 184 and the water flow controlled by a three-way cock.

There is one point which needs watching on such an installation. It may be that the steam pressure is higher than the pressure of the cooling water. If this is so, the entry of the cooling water will be delayed while some of the steam condenses. A blow-off cock of some suitable type should be fitted on the steam header, so that residual steam can be vented before the cooling water is admitted.

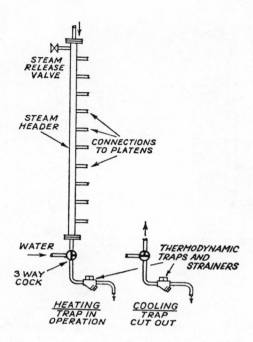

Figure 184

Very often the steam traps draining the platens have insufficient capacity to pass the cooling water at the rate needed to cool the press down quickly and it will be necessary to by-pass them. This is not altogether a bad thing; because if the by-pass is properly used, the condensate from the traps during the heating cycle can be saved for boiler feed, and the cooling water from the by-pass can be diverted to waste, or utilized as hot water.

10 Ship installations

The majority of shipbuilders now give proper attention to the removal of condensate from the very important steam services on board ships. What is bad practice on land is equally bad practice at sea, so far as steam trapping is concerned. There would, indeed, be no need for this chapter were it not for certain jobs which are peculiar to ship practice and certain amendments to land recommendations which are necessary because of the movement of the ship.

The most successful steam traps used on ships are undoubtedly the more robust types that can stand up to the rugged conditions, including waterhammer, vibration and the motion of the ship. The introduction of the thermodynamic type has provided the shipbuilder with a trap which completely meets these requirements and, in addition, is small in size – a most important point, since space is always at a premium on a ship. Other traps are also used successfully, particularly the liquid expansion thermostatic and inverted bucket types.

Main engines and auxiliaries

There is no difference apart from size and complexity between main and auxiliary turbines and the same principles apply to both.

The draining of turbines is discussed in Chapter 11, 'Power plant'. It is, of course, vital that the steam supply should be properly drained, even though superheated steam is used. Any places where condensate could collect must be drained and these include bulkhead stop valves, manoeuvring valves and expansion pieces. Thermodynamic traps are very suitable.

Oil fuel systems

Oil fuel systems will vary in detail from ship to ship but, in general, include bunkers, settling and service tanks and various line heaters, and this equipment is much the same in both turbine and motor ships.

The bunkers and tanks will be heated by steam coils which require careful design and layout if they are to be effective. For proper heat output, the pressure must be kept as high as possible along the full length of the coil which means limiting the maximum length of each coil to about 60 to 75 metres. Condensate has to be properly drained from the coil which should lie flat and without local rises, and at the outlet a water seal and small diameter rising pipe should be used

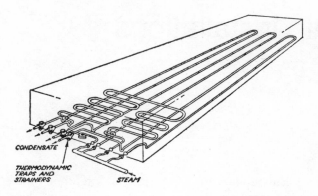

Figure 185

if the trap is fitted above the coil (see also Chapter 3, page 67). As there is almost certain to be some waterhammer, thermodynamic traps are the best choice. Figure 185 shows a typical arrangement in a double bottom tank. Further references to tank coils are made under 'Tanker heating coils' and 'Deep tanks'.

Oil heaters are shell and tube heat exchangers fitted with temperature regulators to maintain the required oil temperature. They are commonly drained by thermodynamic traps but the condensate should not be lifted directly after the traps because of the low steam pressure which can occur due to the action of the control valve. As on land, the condensate should run by gravity to a receiver from which it can be returned by an automatic pump.

Combustion air preheaters

In many boiler installations, combustion air is preheated by a heater battery which may get its heat either from the flue gases before they reach the funnel or by steam bled from the turbine casing. In the latter case, the battery is usually made up of a number of individual sections and each of these should be drained by its own steam trap. Because of the conditions on board ship already referred to, thermodynamic traps are the first choice and if there is a lot of air to be discharged, separate automatic air vents may be needed.

Soot blowers

Soot blowers are fitted to all water tube boilers so that the heating surfaces can be cleaned while the boilers are in service. Superheated steam at boiler pressure is normally used and the steam supply must be drained to prevent any water, which may collect while the blowers are out of use, being picked up by the fast moving steam. Thermodynamic traps are suitable.

A further problem can result from flue gases being drawn into the steam system when steam is turned off, and condensing, producing a vacuum in the supply pipes. This can cause severe corrosion; either the blowers should be completely closed or withdrawn from the flue gases, or a vacuum breaker should be fitted.

Diesel engine cooling systems

When starting main diesel engines, thermal shock and excessive wear are avoided by pre-heating the cooling water and a common method is to use steam coils in the suction tank fitted in the valve and piston cooling circuit and a line heat exchanger in the main jacket circuit. Condensate is best removed by thermodynamic traps.

Whistles

Whistles can be operated by steam or compressed air and steam is often used on motor as well as steam ships. A practical advantage is the characteristic plume of steam which allows other vessels to identify the source of the signal.

Although it may only be used infrequently, the whistle must always be available for instant use so that the steam supply must at all times be properly drained. Figure 186 shows the correct installation with a separator fitted close

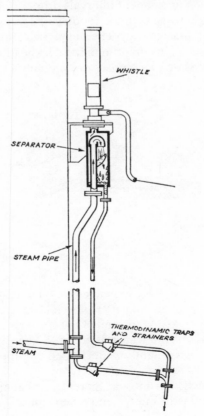

Figure 186

up to the whistle itself to deal with the surge of water which results when the valve is suddenly opened. Water stripped off the pipe wall by the high velocity steam is deflected round and down while steam goes up to the whistle. It is important that the separator should have sufficient capacity to hold the initial rush of water which may easily amount to ten litres or more.

Both this separator and the foot of the rising supply pipe should be drained by thermodynamic traps and where the separator is inside the funnel and consequently more accessible, the drain trap can be fitted about 3.5 m below to allow some spare capacity for any momentary surge of condensate.

Steam mains and deck lines

We have many times stressed the importance of laying out the steam supply system so that condensate runs to adequate drain pockets from which it can be removed by the steam traps. Steam mains supplying galleys, laundries and accommodation and deck lines feeding tank coils and winches are no exception to this rule.

In many cases it is virtually impossible to ensure a proper gradient at all times and this is not helped by the pitching and rolling of the ship. Usually the best that can be done is to provide at frequent intervals proper drain pockets in the form of equal tees and to drain these with thermodynamic traps which will stand up to the waterhammer that must occur. The small size of these traps is a great advantage when draining mains that run in the deckhead where the space is very limited and Figure 187 shows a compact drain point.

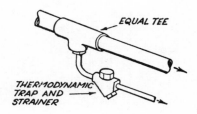

Figure 187

Tanker heating coils

At one time, it was common to try to heat crude oil in tankers by using very long lengths of 40 mm ($1\frac{1}{2}''$) or 50 mm ($2''$) pipe laid in a continuous run on the bottom and sides of the tanks. At the end of the coil a rising pipe of the same size led up to deck level where the trap was fitted. Some of these coils were over 300 m long and were permanently waterlogged for the greater part of their length.

Modern coils are much shorter, and therefore cheaper, and are arranged so that the condensate drains to the far end where there is a loop seal and small bore riser up to the trap. Steam pressure is maintained at a much higher figure along the length of the coil and the heat output is greatly increased for a given weight of coil.

There are three main arrangements of these modern coils. The first is the short coil which is arranged like the traditional long coils on the bottom of the tank. However, instead of one long length it consists of a number of much shorter ones with loop seals and small bore risers.

Then there is the helical coil shown in Figure 188. Containing up to 60 m of 40 mm ($1\frac{1}{2}''$) pipe, this arrangement allows condensate to flow readily to the foot of the rising pipe. In addition, the vertical shape sets up good convection currents in the oil, the whole unit is portable, and the number of coils can be varied to meet particular operating requirements or removed altogether from the tank. Handling is made even easier by fabricating the coil in a number of short, vertical sections which are bolted one on top of the other.

Finally, there is the grid arrangement, one form of which is shown in Figure 189. This coil can be installed easily in the tank but it is sometimes difficult to avoid a preferential flow of steam through some of the legs at the expense of the others and the effect is the same as group trapping. In practice the arrangement seems to work well and is a considerable advance on the old long continuous coils.

Extended surface tubing is also being used for tanker coils since this has a greater area of heating surface per foot run than plain pipe.

Thermodynamic traps are widely used for draining all these modern heating coils. Not only are they rugged enough to stand up to the conditions but their small physical size allows them to fit in to the limited space available.

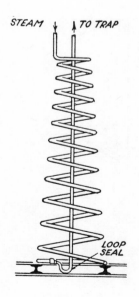

Figure 188

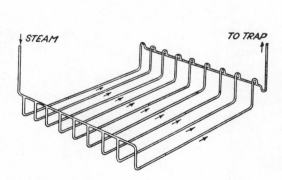

Figure 189

Deep tanks

In addition to tankers with their cargoes of crude oil, an increasing number of dry cargo ships also carry edible oils, molasses and tallow in a molten state in deep tanks.

These, too, are steam heated by continuous or grid type coils. A special problem is that the same tanks are sometimes needed to carry dry cargo and then the heating coils must either be protected by wooden dunnage or else be removed. This has led to the use of external coils formed by welding channels to the underside of the tank bottom. The resulting coil can be either one continuous length or take the form of a grid.

There are a number of new steam problems. In the first place some of these cargoes solidify at relatively high temperatures, which means that not only the tank bottom but also the exposed bulkheads must be provided with heating coils if cold spots are to be avoided. So as to cover these surfaces adequately it is sometimes necessary to have more heating surface than would normally be required just to make good heat losses or raise the cargo through the required temperature range.

Secondly, some of these cargoes are damaged by high temperature in which case steam is used at a relatively low pressure. Finally, the storage temperature is sometimes fairly critical and rapid changes in temperature cannot be tolerated so that automatic temperature regulators are frequently used.

The combination of excessive heating surface and its position on the tank, the low steam pressure and the use of temperature regulators, makes the effective removal of condensate from these coils extremely difficult. Coils or channels on

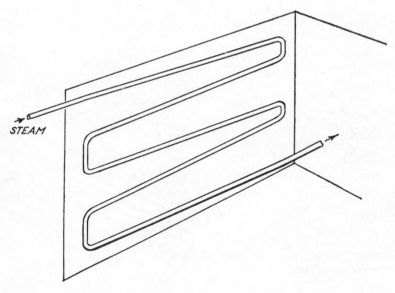

STEAM

Figure 190

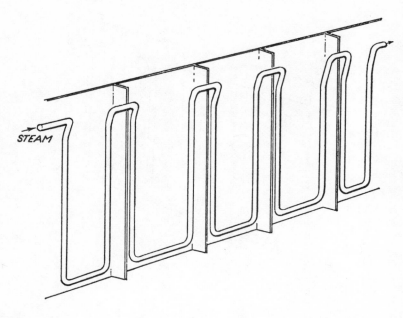

Figure 191

tank bottoms should be kept reasonably short and although a steady fall towards the outlet is impossible the coil should be as level as possible.

Where coils have to be placed on the sides of tanks, the arrangement shown in Figure 190 would be best, but is ruled out in practice because of the frames inside the tank or the corrugated form of the bulkhead, which would cause such a coil to be too far from the ship's side. As a result the layout shown in Figure 191 is frequently adopted. Obviously proper drainage is impossible and condensate will lie in the bottom loops until a drop in cargo temperature causes the regulator to turn on steam and pressure builds up until it is sufficient to clear the condensate rather violently.

Then the coil will be full of steam and overheating may result. Apart from possible damage to the coils due to waterhammer, the temperature regulator will never succeed in holding a steady temperature in the cargo.

In a well designed system the temperature regulator would reduce the steam pressure until the heat emission from the coils just matched the heat requirements of the tank. If the coils were oversized, as they are in this case to get proper coverage of the tank surfaces, the reduction in pressure would eventually cause waterlogging of some of the coil length but gradually and to a controlled extent. But there is nothing controlled about the waterlogging in the Figure 191 arrangement which should be avoided if possible.

Figure 192 shows a much better layout. The coil now takes the form of a grid but the vertical legs can be bent so that they lie close to the hull plates or

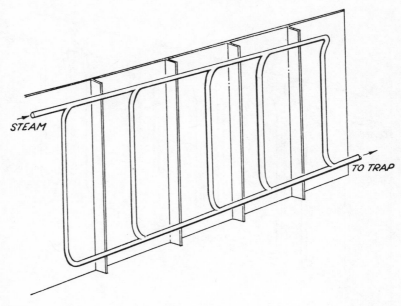

Figure 192

bulkhead. Keeping the headers short and of reasonable bore will help to get even heat distribution.

An advantage over tanker coils is that the drain lines from deep cargo tanks are usually taken out through the bottom or sides of the tanks into the adjacent duct keel or shaft tunnel so there is no problem of lifting condensate up to the traps.

Thermodynamic traps are again indicated because of their small size and ability to stand up to waterhammer, even though the pressure at the trap may at times drop below that required to seat the disc (see Chapter 2, page 35). This low pressure will be caused by the throttling action of the temperature regulator and any steam is likely to have condensed before reaching the end of the coils, so that traps will simply pass condensate without any waste of steam. The traps should be fitted directly on to the coil outlets which normally means putting them in the duct keel or shaft tunnel. Do not fit them in the engine room, which may be 60 m or more away, since this would lead to steam locking.

Because of the low pressure the condensate should drain by gravity to a low level receiver positioned either close to the traps in the duct keel or in the engine room and then be pumped up to the observation tank with an automatic pump.

Heating and air conditioning

In all modern ships warm or cool air is ducted to crew and passenger accommodation. Various systems are used but all include heater batteries either at the central air conditioning unit or at the individual spaces or sometimes at both. These batteries are heated either by steam or hot water, the latter produced by calorifiers. Steam heated batteries and calorifiers must be supplied with dry steam and be properly trapped. The smaller units can be drained by thermodynamic traps but these may have insufficient capacity for the larger ones, in which case inverted bucket traps should be used. The latter may need automatic air vents in parallel with them.

In some systems steam is used for humidification, and for proper control it must be dry. The steam line should be fitted, close to the point of injection, with a steam dryer or separator drained by a thermodynamic trap.

Where radiators and pipe coils are used for accommodation heating, drying rooms or de-icing they should not be grouped to a single large steam trap as used to be common practice. The inevitable result was that much of the heating surface was permanently waterlogged, waterhammer was common and control of temperature impossible.

All radiators and pipe coils should be fitted with small independent traps, the thermodynamic type being best although balanced pressure thermostatic traps can be used.

Laundry equipment

This too is similar to that supplied for land installations and the recommendations already made apply. Thermodynamic traps are commonly used for most laundry equipment including ironers. In the latter case, care should be taken not to fit the traps where they can steam lock and adequate provision must be made for venting air.

Galley equipment

Although there is a trend towards using electricity in galleys steam is still very common. Cooking equipment on board ship is in no way different from that described in Chapter 6 (pages 109–14) and balanced pressure thermostatic traps are widely used. But, whereas on land it is unusual to find thermodynamic traps in kitchens, they are quite often used at sea because of their robust construction.

Because galley steam pressures are never more than about 100 kPa, condensate should not be lifted directly after the steam traps and it is usual for the condensate to flow by gravity to the drain cooler. Under no circumstances should galley drains be connected into return lines carrying condensate from relatively high pressure equipment such as calorifiers. The back pressure in these returns will almost certainly be enough to cause waterlogging of the galley equipment.

11 Steam mains, power plant and compressed air

Some indication of the way in which condensate forms in steam mains and power plant and why it should be removed was given in Chapter 1. The recommended ways of getting rid of it were not discussed there.

Steam mains

Condensate is present in a steam main in two forms, either as water which has separated out from the steam and is running along the wall of the pipe, being deepest at the bottom, or as water particles which are being carried along in the steam flow. The former can be removed directly by a steam trap, but the latter must first be taken out of the steam flow by a steam drier or separator and then discharged by a trap (see Chapter 1, page 23).

In addition to steam and condensate a steam main will also contain air. When the plant is started up from cold, the mains will be full of air and more is likely to come in from the boiler with the steam during normal running, having been liberated from the feed water. Rapid air removal during start-up is particularly important, otherwise the process plant may take a very long time to come up to temperature.

Choice of position

If the steam trap is draining a separator, the trap will be fitted to the bottom outlet and water will flow to it naturally. This is, of course, assuming that the separator is large enough. If it is not, the steam velocity through it may cause water to be picked up again and carried forward. But when the steam trap is draining a main, it is important that it should be so positioned that water will in fact flow to it under all conditions.

The point is mentioned in Chapter 3 (page 51), but it is so important that it should receive further attention. Condensate is being formed all along a steam main; if the main is horizontal with just a slight fall in the direction of flow, the condensate will move forward in a layer along the wall of the pipe. It will be deepest at the bottom and the depth will increase as it gets further from the boiler. If a branch line is taken off from the main and is taken off wrongly, from the bottom, the layer of condensate will run down the hole. If this branch, and all succeeding branches, are taken off, as they should be, from the top, the layer of

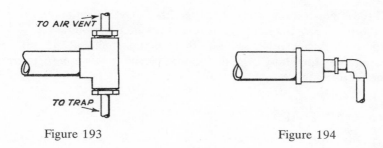

Figure 193   Figure 194

condensate will go forward to the end of the main. Provided that the main is falling all the way, all the condensate which is formed will find its way to the end. This is one certain place where the main should be drained, as shown in Figure 193, and it should be air vented here too. On no account should the main be drained as in Figure 194, that is reduced to the size of the trap inlet by a concentric reducer on the end of the main.

The maximum amount of condensate which is being formed in this horizontal or falling main will depend upon its length, its diameter and the dryness fraction of the steam. The greatest load will be on warming up, so that the efficiency of the lagging, if any, will affect only the running and not the maximum load. Although the main is drained at the end, this may not be enough. As a rough guide horizontal mains should be drained about every 30 to 50 m.

The choice of position for these intermediate drains rather depends on circumstances. Often a main will not, in fact, run horizontal or falling for the distances mentioned. If it does, the drain point should be put in as convenient in the form of a full-sized tee, Figure 195. Should there be a reducing valve or a steam meter in this length, the drain point would be chosen immediately before this restriction. A globe valve in the line should, if possible, be fitted with the stem horizontal to avoid forming a water pocket; so also should a lyre type expansion bend.

What is more probable is that the main will have to rise somewhere in the length. In this case the main must most certainly be drained immediately before the rise, Figure 196. Alternatively there may be a low point in the line, where the main passes under an obstruction. This too should be drained just before the rise.

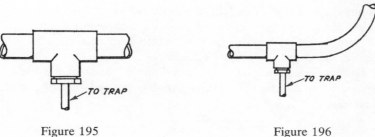

Figure 195   Figure 196

In all these illustrations a full sized tee has been shown as the drain pocket. This is the best recommendation, as it ensures that all condensate shall in fact reach the trap. At the other extreme there is the small, say, 15 mm ($\frac{1}{2}''$) drain point taken away hopefully from the bottom of, say, a 150 mm (6") main. This is quite ineffective.

Choice of trap

The type of trap to be chosen for these drains depends upon many circumstances. If the steam is superheated and at high pressure, then traps of the thermodynamic or inverted bucket types, specially built of materials to suit these conditions, are best. At lower pressures float and balanced pressure thermostatic traps can be used, especially on branch lines to process plant.

Bimetallic traps are sometimes used for draining steam mains, particularly on large outdoor sites, where condensate collection is impracticable. Their continuous action and the reduction in the amount of flash steam formed is then preferred to the blast discharge of some of the other types. But don't forget that this is only happening because condensate is being held back by the trap until it has cooled down below steam temperature, so that a really adequate cooling leg is essential if condensate is to be cleared from the main.

Traps of the balanced-pressure thermostatic type should also be fitted after a collecting pocket in which condensate can lie while it is losing its temperature. Inverted bucket traps, when used for draining mains, should have a check valve on the inlet to prevent loss of water seal due to superheat or a sudden pressure drop in the main. In some cases these traps are supplied with a special check valve already fitted into the inlet passage in the body. In all cases the use of a strainer before the trap is recommended and some traps are fitted with an integral screen.

Since traps vary in their capacity for handling air, it may be necessary to fit separate air vents in parallel with traps on intermediate drain points on long mains.

A final point concerns the type of trap to use if it has to discharge into a return line already practically full of condensate that may have cooled down well below steam temperature. This can happen, for example, where condensate from a number of traps on a site is collected and pumped back to the feed tank. If the return line runs close to the steam main, it is tempting to discharge the traps on the main drain points into it. In these circumstances flash steam from these traps will condense in the cooler condensate in the return and may cause quite severe waterhammer and noise. This will obviously be worst where the traps have a blast action and discharge condensate at steam temperature.

If this method of collecting the condensate from the traps on the main is unavoidable, the use of a continuous discharge float trap may well overcome the trouble. Otherwise a bimetallic trap discharging condensate continuously below steam temperature can be used, providing that the precautions outlined above have been taken.

Frost

The draining of outside mains requires that precautions should be taken against frost and this matter has already been mentioned in Chapter 3 (page 64), where it is suggested that those thermodynamic and bimetallic traps which are not damaged when frozen should be used.

If traps which can be damaged by freezing are used then they must be protected by fully waterproofed lagging which must at the same time be removable so that maintenance work can be carried out. Lagging can only be used in the case of those traps which continue to operate when the escape of heat is prevented.

Vibration

The choice of steam trap is sometimes affected by the type of plant which the main is feeding. For example, a main feeding steam hammers may be subject to violent vibration and a similar condition may be set up by the valve action of a reciprocating engine. By far the best trap for these conditions is the thermodynamic type but liquid expansion thermostatic traps can also be used.

Sizing and layout

Correct sizing of a steam main is of the greatest importance so as to prevent excessively high velocities and ensure that there is a reasonable pressure drop to the points from which the process or power plant is fed. Appendix 1 deals with the sizing of saturated steam pipes. If the steam carries much superheat, sizing and installation call for specialist knowledge.

Mains should be laid so that there is a fall in the direction of flow of at least 12 mm in 3 m. They should be securely anchored and proper provision made for expansion so that, as they heat up, they retain their correct shape, allowing condensate to flow freely to the drain point. Sagging steam mains are a prime cause of waterhammer. Finally, proper lagging is essential to reduce loss of heat and therefore condensation in the mains to a minimum. Particular care must be taken with the lagging when mains run out of doors and are exposed to the weather.

Power plant

The draining and air venting of certain power plant auxiliaries, such as feed water heaters and evaporators, have already been considered.

The presence of condensate in engines themselves may be due to three reasons. It may come in with the steam; it may be formed by the loss of heat to the cylinder walls; it may be formed because of the heat drop in the steam during expansion.

Steam feed

The main reason for supplying power plant with superheated steam is to obtain the greatest possible power output, but an added advantage is that water is not carried into the engine due to condensation in the main. If the engine is supplied with steam which is dry and saturated at the boiler, it will be wet by the time the engine is reached. The main will presumably have been drained, but a separator

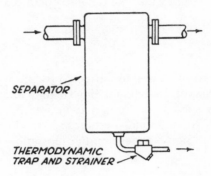

Figure 197

should be fitted immediately before entry to the engine. The use of saturated and not superheated steam rather suggests that this is a small and simple plant with a reciprocating engine and not a turbine. Figure 197 shows a layout of a separator being drained with a thermodynamic trap. This trap is chosen because it has ample capacity and at the same time is not affected by vibration or flutter. An inverted bucket trap could also be used.

Engine cylinders

The cylinders and valve chests of reciprocating engines are provided with drain connections and these are normally fitted with cocks. In some cases steam traps have successfully replaced these cocks, but many engineers prefer to drain the condensate out manually, particularly when the engines run continuously, since the failure of a trap could cause very serious damage to the engine. Either thermodynamic or liquid expansion thermostatic traps can be used since both types will stand up to the vibration and pulsation produced when the engine is running.

It has been said that the condensation due to steam expansion in a simple reciprocating engine will be carried out by the exhaust. This is so when the engine is running. But many engines of this type are not drained when warming up or standing. Condensation in the cylinders of engines which are used only intermittently may be a great nuisance – in colliery winding engines, for example, where these are still steam driven. One pit accident, when the cage overran, was due to water in the cylinders.

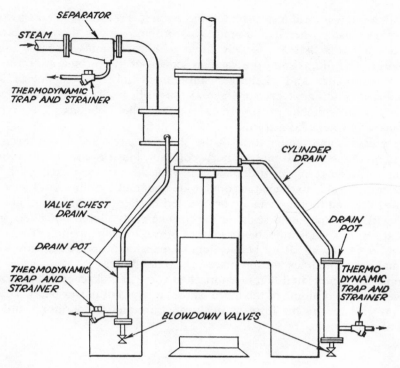

Figure 198

Water in the cylinders of steam hammers is a particular source of complaint by the operators. This collects not only because of intermittent working but also due to priming of the boiler which can readily occur when a large hammer starts up. All this leads to short life of gland packings and heavy maintenance as well as making sensitive control of the hammer stroke difficult.

Figure 198 shows the best way to drain a hammer using thermodynamic traps which are not affected by the very considerable vibration produced when the hammer is working. A separator in the steam supply makes sure that dry steam reaches the valve chest and considerably improves control of the stroke. The valve chest and cylinder drains are connected to reservoir pots firmly fixed to the frame and each of these is drained by a thermodynamic trap. The pots will take care of any sudden rush of water caused by priming and a blow down cock on the bottom of each pot can be used to blow off any oil that collects.

Turbines

When the power plant to be drained is a turbine problems of vibration do not arise. The steam mains will need draining by an inlet separator because, even if the steam is superheated, there is the warming-up period to be considered. Temperature and pressure conditions will probably indicate the use of a thermodynamic or inverted bucket trap.

Condensate will form inside the turbine when it is warming up and also as the result of expansion when it is running. The turbine casing is, therefore, provided with drain points that are usually fitted with cocks and discharge into the condenser. The drains from the vacuum section of the turbine are often fitted with orifice plates and discharge continuously into the condenser, which maintains a differential pressure across the orifice. The drain cocks can be replaced with suitable steam traps so that the condensate is removed automatically whenever it forms.

The pressure and temperature of the steam at any stage in the turbine will depend on the load. This may be fairly constant, but it is also possible for wide fluctuations to take place. It depends on what the turbine is doing. The traps chosen must be able to discharge condensate under all conditions of temperature and pressure and thermodynamic or inverted bucket traps are generally used.

It is vital that the gland seals on the turbine shaft should not flood and the gland steam pipe runs must be drained to prevent this happening. Because the pressure is usually 35 kPa or below, liquid expansion traps are the most suitable type and are sometimes used in place of manual drains.

It must be appreciated that no more than very general recommendations can be given for the draining of the more elaborate types of power plant. There are so many variables in the form of steam pressure and temperature, duties and types of units.

Compressed air drainage

Compressed air operated equipment is now so widely used that there are few works which do not have a compressed air system. As with a steam plant, compressed air is generally required at the point of usage dry and at the right pressure. This means that the air mains must be correctly sized and laid so that the water reaches the various drain points and branches to the equipment should be taken off the top of the main. In fact the rules are very much the same as those for steam.

In much the same way as steam, but for quite different reasons, compressed air gives up moisture as it cools. The act of compression raises the temperature of the air and, although it may be passed through an aftercooler, it still has heat to lose before it reaches the place where it is to be used.

It is not unusual to release the water from compressed air mains and receivers by means of hand operated drain cocks. Now we have seen that such cocks are a poor way of getting water out of steam equipment; they are even less effective for getting water out of compressed air. Steam has a way of advertising its presence when it is being blown to waste, but compressed air has not. Since compressed air at 700 kPa blowing to waste through a 3 mm hole wastes about 12 dm^3 of free air per second it is as well to consider what other means besides drain cocks there are for getting the water out of the air.

The uses of compressed air fall, very roughly, into two groups. In the first come such things as pneumatic tools, riveters and coal cutters for which it is generally sufficient to remove the water which has already separated out from the air. The second group includes paint sprays, foundry mould blowing, pneumatic control equipment and the multitude of small air operated rams used on all sorts of machines in factories ranging from laundries to engineering machine and assembly shops. Here the ideal is to get out even the particles of water that are being carried in the air stream.

Water which has separated out is present in the air main or receiver as a layer of water, very much like water in a steam main. This can be removed, following general steam trapping lines, by a float trap. The drainage point must be carefully chosen, so that the water can really get down to the trap. Figure 199 shows how a main is being drained at a point where it rises. This so far is standard steam trapping practice. But if the traps can air bind on a steam line, it is clearly possible for them to air bind on an air line. And the fitting of an air vent doesn't cure this trouble.

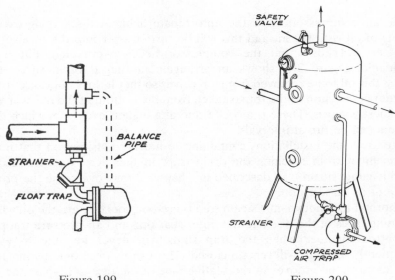

Figure 199   Figure 200

For water to flow into a trap on a compressed air system, it is necessary that it should be able to displace air from the body of the trap. If the amount of water coming into the trap is small, as is usually the case with an air main drain point, it is possible for it to trickle down the wall of the pipe to the trap, displacing air up the centre. But if there is a lot of water, as is likely with a compressed air receiver, this may not happen and a balance pipe must be provided from the top of the trap to a point above the possible water level in the equipment being drained. Air is then displaced up this balance pipe by the incoming water to the trap. Figure 200 shows an air receiver properly fitted up with a balance pipe. The balance pipe in Figure 199 is shown dotted because, as already indicated, it may not be required.

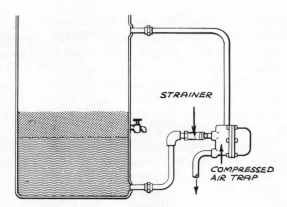

Figure 201

Some air compressors have the unfortunate habit of discharging excessive amounts of oil with the air and this will be carried over into the receiver. It is usually an indication that the compressor needs overhauling but if it is unavoidable, Figure 201 shows an arrangement that is often successful in allowing this oil to be removed from a receiver so that it does not cause trouble. The water connection to the trap is taken from the bottom of the receiver where the cleanest water is. There is a cock fitted at a higher level from which the oil and scum can be run at intervals.

There are some installations containing so much emulsified oil that nothing will prevent it from reaching the drain trap. In these cases a variant of the thermodynamic steam trap described in Chapter 2 may overcome the problem because of its blast action.

If a normal thermodynamic steam trap is used on cool oily air, the oil will seal the seating faces of the disc and the outer seat ring and air pressure trapped in the control chamber when the trap shuts will never be able to escape. Consequently the trap will remain closed. This can be overcome by machining one or more radial grooves in the seating face of the disc to by-pass the outer seat ring and allow pressure to escape slowly from the control chamber, so that the trap operates at a normal rate. Some experimenting may be necessary on the job to get the size of these grooves just right for the amount and viscosity of oil to be handled but for those prepared to do this, the thermodynamic trap may well provide an answer to a very difficult problem.

The complete drying of compressed air for spray guns, instruments, pneumatic actuators and the like is more difficult since this requires that the water particles in the air shall be removed. The first step is to fit an efficient aftercooler between the compressor and the receiver so that as much of the moisture as possible is separated out before the air reaches the distribution mains. This aftercooler will need draining in a similar manner to the receiver (Figure 200).

It may then be sufficient to fit an air separator in the main, in just the same way as a steam separator is fitted to improve steam quality. An air separator

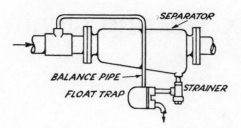

Figure 202

works in just the same way as a steam separator and water particles are removed because of their greater density than the air which carries them. The separator should be drained as shown in Figure 202.

But even a separator on the main will not give dry enough air for some jobs. Many of these need, in addition, a small filter fitted right on the job and the water should be removed by an automatic drain trap fitted to the bottom of the filter bowl. In the case of some special applications the air is passed through a chemical such as silica gel, which absorbs the finest water particles.

Appendix 1 Sizing steam pipes

The theory

The incorrect sizing of steam pipes can lead either to steam starvation at the steam using end, if the pipes are too small, or to undue capital cost and waste by radiation if the pipes are too large. Since steam starvation can give rise to troubles for which steam traps are sometimes blamed, it is not perhaps out of place to describe one practical and comparatively simple means by which the correct sizes of steam pipes can be determined.

The theory upon which the method and the tables are based was the work of Wierz of Charlottenburg and was developed by him in conjunction with Brabbée. The tables have been further simplified for everyday use.

The original equation upon which the tables are based uses imperial units of measurement and is

$$\frac{p_1^{1.9375} - p_2^{1.9375}}{L} = 0.00012 \frac{Q^{1.853}}{d^{4.987}}$$

p_1 is the initial pressure at the beginning of a run of pipe.
p_2 is the final pressure at the end of a run of pipe.
L is the equivalent length (ft) of the pipe after the resistance of fittings has been taken into account.
Q is the quantity of steam passing (lb per hour).
d is the diameter of the pipe (in.).

The various constants were settled by experimental work at Charlottenburg. The practical value of the tables and the method has been demonstrated by constant and successful use.

The tables

These are in two parts, A and B, in which the original imperial units have been replaced by metric ones. Considering the information in Table A, the left hand column $F = \dfrac{P_1 - P_2}{L}$ and corresponds to the left hand side of the original equation, being a series of factors based on the pressure drop per metre of pipe.

Under the various sizes of steam mains (d of the equation) there are two horizontal lines X and Y for each pressure drop factor.

X gives the quantity of steam in kg/s passed by each size of pipe for the various pressure drop factors (*Q* of the equation).

Y gives a velocity factor in m/s of the A quantity of steam passing.

Table B gives a rapid means of finding the pressure drop factor $\dfrac{P_1 - P_2}{L}$ thus:

Suppose the initial pressure at entry to the pipe (p_1) is 700 kPa gauge, then the pressure factor (P_1) is, from Table B, 56.38.

Suppose the final pressure at the end of the pipe (p_2) is 650 kPa gauge, then P_2 is 49.76.

If the length of the pipe (inclusive of allowances for bends, fittings, etc.) is 221 metres, then

$$\frac{P_1 - P_2}{L} = F = \frac{56.38 - 49.76}{221} = 0.030$$

From Table A we can see that, following down the left hand column to 0.030 and then reading to the right, a 65 mm (2½″) pipe, for example, will carry 0.255 kg of steam per second (*X*) with a velocity factor (*Y*) of 80.64.

The velocity factor (*Y*) is based on a steam volume of 1 m³/kg and can readily be converted to give the true velocity for any other volume.

So $Y = \dfrac{\text{True velocity} \times 1}{\text{Actual volume}}$

Returning to our example, *Y* = 80.64 and the volume of steam at 700 kPa is 0.24 m³/kg, so $80.64 = \dfrac{\text{True velocity}}{0.24}$

So True velocity = 80.64 × 0.24
               = 19.35 m/s

Two other factors remain to be discussed. The first is the allowance to be made for bends and fittings in deciding the effective length of the pipe (*L*).

A simple, but practical, rule is: add 10 % to the true length on a job where the travel is more than 100 m and the line is reasonably straight: add 20 % when the travel is less than 100 m.

The second point is to give some guidance about velocities in saturated steam mains. Practical experience shows that reasonable velocities are 25 to 35 m/s. Above 35 m/s noise and erosion are likely, particularly if the steam is wet. In short branch connections even these figures may be too high if a high pressure drop is to be avoided and it would be better not to exceed 15 m/s.

Use of tables

In deciding the size of main to pass a given quantity of steam there are three unknowns:
(a) The size of main
(b) The velocity of steam through it
(c) The pressure drop along it

Table A   Pipe sizes

F		15 mm ½"	20 mm ¾"	25 mm 1"	32 mm 1¼"	40 mm 1½"	50 mm 2"	65 mm 2½"	80 mm 3"	100 mm 4"	125 mm 5"	150 mm 6"	175 mm 7"	200 mm 8"	225 mm 9"	250 mm 10"	300 mm 12"
0·00016	x						0·0084	0·0154	0·0252	0·0553	0·1000	0·1662	0·2472	0·3542	0·4375	0·6469	1·056
	y						4·30	4·86	5·55	6·82	7·90	9·16	10·05	10·94	11·94	12·77	14·54
0·00020	x					0·0045	0·0095	0·0174	0·0286	0·0627	0·1131	0·1839	0·2792	0·3992	0·5461	0·7286	1·188
	y					3·96	4·85	5·51	6·31	7·72	8·92	10·13	11·34	12·33	13·37	14·58	16·36
0·00025	x				0·0030	0·0050	0·0106	0·0193	0·0314	0·0694	0·1250	0·2043	0·3078	0·4661	0·6064	0·8067	1·310
	y				3·74	4·39	5·40	6·08	6·92	8·56	9·87	11·26	12·51	14·40	14·85	15·92	18·04
0·00030	x				0·0033	0·0054	0·0116	0·0211	0·0345	0·0753	0·1366	0·2237	0·3358	0·4814	0·6639	0·8811	1·430
	y				4·13	4·73	5·92	6·65	7·60	9·29	10·79	12·31	13·65	14·87	16·26	17·39	19·70
0·00035	x		0·0010	0·0019	0·0035	0·0057	0·0122	0·0223	0·0361	0·0793	0·1442	0·2348	0·3553	0·5064	0·6936	0·9294	1·502
	y		3·54	3·88	4·30	5·04	6·21	7·04	7·96	9·77	11·38	12·94	14·44	15·64	17·00	18·34	20·69
0·00045	x		0·0011	0·0022	0·0040	0·0065	0·0141	0·0257	0·0419	0·0926	0·1679	0·2721	0·4106	0·5883	0·8092	1·079	1·741
	y		3·96	4·49	5·03	5·73	7·18	8·13	9·24	11·42	13·26	15·00	16·68	18·18	19·82	21·29	23·99
0·00055	x		0·0012	0·0025	0·0045	0·0074	0·0159	0·0288	0·0474	0·1036	0·1873	0·3058	0·4619	0·6617	0·9114	1·205	1·960
	y		4·37	5·09	5·59	6·49	8·08	9·10	10·46	12·78	14·78	16·85	18·77	20·44	22·32	23·78	27·01
0·00065	x		0·0014	0·0027	0·0049	0·0081	0·0173	0·0316	0·0579	0·1138	0·2055	0·3353	0·5064	0·7208	0·9992	1·328	2·150
	y		4·77	5·41	6·13	7·14	8·82	9·98	11·43	14·04	16·22	18·48	20·58	22·27	24·47	26·21	29·62
0·00075	x		0·0015	0·0029	0·0054	0·0088	0·0189	0·0345	0·0564	0·1239	0·2235	0·3653	0·5492	0·7878	1·0856	1·437	2·324
	y		5·41	5·98	6·67	7·77	9·62	10·88	12·44	15·28	17·64	20·13	22·32	24·34	26·59	28·35	32·02
0·00085	x		0·0016	0·0033	0·0061	0·0100	0·0214	0·0391	0·0639	0·1404	0·2533	0·4139	0·6222	0·8931	1·230	1·628	2·634
	y		5·72	6·78	7·56	8·80	10·91	12·34	14·09	17·32	19·99	22·81	25·29	27·59	30·13	32·13	36·29
0·00100	x	0·0005	0·0017	0·0035	0·0065	0·0106	0·0227	0·0413	0·0681	0·1498	0·2690	0·4386	0·6675	0·9337	1·307	1·730	2·792
	y	4·10	6·13	7·21	8·12	9·37	11·58	13·03	15·01	18·48	21·24	24·17	27·13	29·03	32·02	34·14	38·47
0·00125	x	0·0006	0·0020	0·0038	0·0069	0·0113	0·0243	0·0444	0·0727	0·1605	0·2883	0·4719	0·7067	1·009	1·399	1·849	2·955
	y	4·39	7·20	7·68	8·62	9·97	12·39	14·02	16·03	19·80	22·76	26·01	28·72	31·19	34·26	36·48	40·71
0·00150	x	0·0007	0·0021	0·0042	0·0078	0·0128	0·0275	0·0498	0·0820	0·1813	0·3256	0·5300	0·8044	1·136	1·564	2·081	3·333
	y	5·00	7·36	8·58	9·68	11·26	13·98	15·72	18·07	22·37	25·70	29·21	32·69	35·11	38·31	41·08	45·92
0·00175	x	0·0007	0·0024	0·0045	0·0082	0·0137	0·0287	0·0524	0·0864	0·1907	0·3528	0·5603	0·8461	1·192	1·645	2·181	3·635
	y	5·19	8·40	9·22	10·23	12·08	14·63	16·56	19·05	23·52	27·85	30·88	34·39	36·83	40·28	43·04	50·08
0·0020	x	0·0008	0·0026	0·0052	0·0094	0·0157	0·0328	0·0599	0·0988	0·2179	0·4031	0·6403	0·9672	1·362	1·880	2·493	4·154
	y	5·94	9·29	10·54	11·68	13·81	16·72	18·93	21·77	26·88	31·82	35·28	39·31	42·09	46·04	49·19	57·24
0·0025	x	0·0009	0·0029	0·0058	0·0103	0·0170	0·0367	0·0668	0·1087	0·2449	0·4322	0·7072	1·061	1·506	2·096	2·803	4·584
	y	6·61	10·13	11·74	12·86	15·01	18·67	21·09	23·96	30·21	34·12	38·97	43·11	46·53	51·33	55·31	63·16
0·0030	x	0·0010	0·0035	0·0063	0·0112	0·0185	0·0398	0·0728	0·1194	0·2618	0·4725	0·7686	1·162	1·686	2·299	3·065	5·006
	y	7·20	12·25	12·73	13·97	16·33	20·29	22·98	26·32	32·29	37·30	42·36	47·22	52·08	56·30	60·48	68·97
0·0040	x	0·0012	0·0039	0·0075	0·0135	0·0225	0·0481	0·0872	0·1430	0·3133	0·5667	0·9250	1·403	2·002	2·751	3·678	6·007
	y	8·73	13·83	15·26	16·77	19·82	24·49	27·52	31·53	38·65	44·73	50·97	57·02	61·86	67·39	72·58	82·76
0·0050	x	0·0013	0·0044	0·0084	0·0153	0·0251	0·0545	0·0983	0·1607	0·3542	0·6403	1·035	1·594	2·275	3·133	4·127	6·797
	y	9·86	15·37	17·20	18·97	22·10	27·74	31·05	35·43	43·68	50·54	57·05	64·76	70·28	76·73	81·45	93·64
0·0060	x	0·0015	0·0051	0·0099	0·0168	0·0275	0·0599	0·1090	0·1798	0·3922	0·7083	1·152	1·744	2·520	3·446	4·577	7·492
	y	10·99	17·97	20·26	20·83	24·26	30·53	34·41	39·63	48·38	55·92	63·50	70·86	77·86	84·40	90·32	103·2
0·0080	x	0·0017	0·0057	0·0109	0·0195	0·0323	0·0699	0·1267	0·2084	0·4578	0·8267	1·355	2·043	2·929	4·005	5·326	8·718
	y	12·72	20·22	22·20	24·22	28·46	35·58	40·00	45·95	56·46	65·26	74·69	83·03	90·48	98·09	105·1	120·1
0·0100	x	0·0019	0·0062	0·0123	0·0221	0·0362	0·0789	0·1430	0·2350	0·5175	0·9261	1·630	2·316	3·296	4·522	5·993	9·807
	y	14·36	21·75	24·97	27·44	31·94	40·16	45·16	51·80	63·83	73·11	84·07	94·11	101·8	110·8	118·3	135·1
0·0125	x	0·0020		0·0131	0·0225	0·0389	0·0839	0·1520	0·2505	0·5508	0·9969	1·730	2·457	3·527	4·841	6·409	10·46
	y	15·38		26·75	27·98	34·31	42·74	48·00	55·22	67·94	78·70	89·81	99·84	109·0	118·5	126·5	144·6

		0.0023	0.0069	0.0148	0.0266	0.0437	.0950	0.1724	0.2833	0.6194	1.124	1.839	2.784	3.959	5.440	7.215	11.84
0.0150	x	0.0023	0.0069	0.0148	0.0266	0.0437	.0950	0.1724	0.2833	0.6194	1.124	1.839	2.784	3.959	5.440	7.215	11.84
	y	17.31	24.49	30.18	33.03	38.50	48.38	54.43	62.46	76.40	88.70	101.3	113.1	122.3	133.2	142.4	163.1
0.0175	x	0.0024	0.0073	0.0155	0.0279	0.0460	0.1001	0.1848	0.2981	0.6555	1.192	1.943	2.920	4.171	5.721	7.628	12.28
	y	17.95	25.85	31.56	34.68	40.65	50.99	58.34	65.70	80.52	94.09	107.1	118.7	128.9	140.1	150.5	169.1
0.020	x	0.0027	0.0084	0.0177	0.0319	0.0526	0.1144	0.2111	0.3406	0.7492	1.362	2.220	3.337	4.767	6.538	8.718	14.03
	y	20.51	29.55	36.07	39.62	46.36	58.27	66.67	75.01	92.41	107.5	122.3	135.6	147.3	160.1	172.0	193.3
0.025	x	0.0031	0.0093	0.0196	0.0354	0.0583	0.1277	0.2318	0.3797	0.8250	1.506	2.449	3.693	5.370	7.321	9.653	15.72
	y	23.00	32.80	40.02	43.97	51.39	65.03	73.20	83.70	101.7	118.9	135.0	150.1	165.9	179.3	190.5	216.5
0.03	x	0.0033	0.0102	0.0214	0.0383	0.0639	0.1392	0.2554	0.4111	0.9067	1.634	2.720	4.022	5.810	7.943	10.47	17.37
	y	25.11	36.03	43.70	47.63	56.31	70.89	80.64	90.62	111.8	129.0	149.9	163.5	179.5	194.5	206.6	239.3
0.04	x	0.0040	0.0123	0.0259	0.0470	0.0776	0.1669	0.3036	0.4972	1.090	1.975	3.228	4.849	7.015	9.603	12.67	20.84
	y	30.26	43.23	52.72	58.44	68.46	84.98	95.87	109.6	134.4	155.9	177.9	197.1	216.7	235.2	250.0	287.1
0.05	x	0.0046	0.0138	0.0290	0.0531	0.0872	0.1880	0.3419	0.5611	1.226	2.234	3.623	5.381	7.900	10.90	14.30	23.70
	y	34.38	48.52	59.08	66.04	76.86	95.73	108.0	123.7	151.2	176.3	199.7	218.7	244.1	266.9	282.3	326.5
0.06	x	0.0050	0.0147	0.0321	0.0586	0.0953	0.2084	0.3814	0.6197	1.349	2.452	3.991	5.912	8.718	11.99	15.94	
	y	37.96	51.88	65.47	72.81	84.06	106.1	120.4	136.6	166.3	193.5	219.9	240.2	269.3	293.6	314.5	
0.08	x	0.0059	0.0173	0.0374	0.0681	0.1117	0.2424	0.4428	0.7219	1.580	2.847	4.631	6.811	10.15			
	y	44.11	61.02	76.28	86.69	98.49	123.5	139.8	159.1	194.9	224.7	255.2	276.8	313.5			
0.10	x	0.0067	0.0195	0.0422	0.0769	0.1267	0.2724	0.5011	0.8172	1.784	3.201	5.244	7.628				
	y	50.29	68.70	86.01	95.67	111.7	138.7	158.2	180.1	220.1	252.7	289.0	310.0				
0.12	x	0.0072	0.0215	0.0466	0.0851	0.1389	0.2997	0.5517	0.8989	1.975	3.528						
	y	54.39	75.91	94.90	105.9	122.5	152.6	174.2	198.1	243.6	278.5						
0.15	x	0.0079	0.0234	0.0511	0.0928	0.1532	0.3319	0.6003	0.9706	2.158							
	y	59.64	82.42	104.1	115.4	135.1	169.0	189.5	213.9	266.2							
0.20	x	0.0095	0.0283	0.0613	0.1117	0.1839	0.3964	0.7219	1.171	2.588							
	y	71.82	99.93	124.9	138.9	162.1	201.9	228.0	258.2	319.2							
0.25	x	0.0105	0.0313	0.0681	0.1244	0.2043	0.4347	0.7989	1.297								
	y	78.94	110.4	138.7	154.7	180.1	221.4	252.3	285.8								
0.30	x	0.0115	0.0341	0.0741	0.1354	0.2235	0.4750	0.8683	1.405								
	y	86.58	120.2	150.9	168.3	197.0	241.9	274.2	309.6								
0.35	x	0.0120	0.0357	0.0787	0.1430	0.2336	0.5006	0.9058									
	y	90.70	126.1	160.2	177.8	206.0	254.9	286.0									
0.40	x	0.0139	0.0409	0.0899	0.1634	0.2670	0.5719	1.035									
	y	104.5	144.1	183.1	203.2	235.4	291.3	326.9									
0.45	x	0.0140	0.0417	0.0907	0.1667	0.2721	0.5786										
	y	105.3	146.9	184.8	207.3	239.9	294.7										
0.50	x	0.0155	0.0463	0.1008	0.1852	0.3025	0.6428										
	y	117.0	163.3	205.3	230.3	266.7	327.4										
0.60	x	0.0173	0.0515	0.1117	0.2043	0.3336											
	y	130.3	181.5	227.5	254.0	294.1											
0.70	x	0.0175	0.0524	0.1132	0.2086												
	y	132.0	185.0	230.6	259.3												
0.80	x	0.0200	0.0599	0.1294	0.2384												
	y	150.8	211.4	263.6	296.4												
0.90	x	0.0204	0.0607	0.1324													
	y	153.3	214.0	269.7													

x   Steam Passed in kg/s
y   Velocity Factor

Table B

Pressure kPa abs	Volume m³/kg	Pressure Factor	Pressure kPa gauge	Volume m³/kg	Pressure Factor	Pressure kPa gauge	Volume m³/kg	Pressure Factor
5	28·19	0·0301	215	0·576	9·309	770	0·222	66·31
10	14·67	0·0115	220	0·568	9·597	780	0·219	67·79
15	10·02	0·0253	225	0·560	9·888	790	0·217	69·29
20	7·649	0·0442	230	0·552	10·18	800	0·215	70·80
25	6·204	0·0681	235	0·544	10·48	810	0·212	72·33
30	5·229	0·0970	240	0·536	10·79	820	0·210	73·88
35	4·530	0·1308	245	0·529	11·10	830	0·208	75·44
40	3·993	0·1694	250	0·522	11·41	840	0·206	77·02
45	3·580	0·2128	255	0·515	11·72	850	0·204	78·61
50	3·240	0·2610	260	0·509	12·05	860	0·202	80·22
55	2·964	0·3140	265	0·502	12·37	870	0·200	81·84
60	2·732	0·3716	270	0·496	12·70	880	0·198	83·49
65	2·535	0·4340	275	0·489	13·03	890	0·196	85·14
70	2·365	0·5010	280	0·483	13·37	900	0·194	86·81
75	2·217	0·5727	285	0·477	13·71	910	0·192	88·50
80	2·087	0·6489	290	0·471	14·06	920	0·191	90·20
85	1·972	0·7298	295	0·466	14·41	930	0·189	91·92
90	1·869	0·8153	300	0·461	14·76	940	0·187	93·66
95	1·777	0·9053	310	0·451	15·48	950	0·185	95·41
101·3	1·673	1·025	320	0·440	16·22	960	0·184	97·18
kPa gauge			330	0·431	16·98	970	0·182	98·96
0	1·673	1·025	340	0·422	17·75	980	0·181	100·75
5	1·601	1·126	350	0·413	18·54	990	0·179	102·57
10	1·533	1·230	360	0·405	19·34	1000	0·177	104·40
15	1·471	1·339	370	0·396	20·16	1020	0·174	108·10
20	1·414	1·453	380	0·389	21·00	1040	0·172	111·87
25	1·361	1·572	390	0·381	21·85	1060	0·169	115·70
30	1·312	1·694	400	0·374	22·72	1080	0·166	119·59
35	1·268	1·822	410	0·367	23·61	1100	0·163	123·54
40	1·225	1·953	420	0·361	24·51	1120	0·161	127·56
45	1·186	2·090	430	0·355	25·43	1140	0·158	131·64
50	1·149	2·230	440	0·348	26·36	1160	0·156	135·78
55	1·115	2·375	450	0·342	27·32	1180	0·153	139·98
60	1·083	2·525	460	0·336	28·28	1200	0·151	144·25
65	1·051	2·679	470	0·330	29·27	1220	0·149	148·57
70	1·024	2·837	480	0·325	30·27	1240	0·147	152·96
75	0·997	2·999	490	0·320	31·29	1260	0·145	157·41
80	0·971	3·166	500	0·315	32·32	1280	0·143	161·92
85	0·946	3·338	510	0·310	33·37	1300	0·141	166·50
90	0·923	3·514	520	0·305	34·44	1320	0·139	171·13
95	0·901	3·694	530	0·301	35·52	1340	0·135	175·83
100	0·881	3·878	540	0·296	36·62	1360	0·133	180·58
105	0·860	4·067	550	0·292	37·73	1380	0·132	185·40
110	0·841	4·260	560	0·288	38·36	1400	0·130	190·29
115	0·823	4·458	570	0·284	40·01	1420	0·128	195·23
120	0·806	4·660	580	0·280	41·17	1440	0·127	200·23
125	0·788	4·866	590	0·276	42·35	1460	0·125	205·30
130	0·773	5·076	600	0·272	43·54	1480	0·124	210·42
135	0·757	5·291	610	0·269	44·76	1500	0·122	215·61
140	0·743	5·510	620	0·265	45·98	1520	0·121	220·86
145	0·728	5·734	630	0·261	47·23	1540	0·119	226·17
150	0·714	5·961	640	0·258	48·48	1560	0·118	231·54
155	0·701	6·193	650	0·255	49·76	1580	0·117	236·97
160	0·689	6·429	660	0·252	51·05	1600	0·115	242·46
165	0·677	6·670	670	0·249	52·36	1620	0·114	248·01
170	0·665	6·915	680	0·246	53·68	1640	0·113	253·62
175	0·654	7·164	690	0·243	55·02	1660	0·111	259·30
180	0·643	7·417	700	0·240	56·38	1680	0·110	265·03
185	0·632	7·675	710	0·237	57·75	1700	0·109	270·83
190	0·622	7·937	720	0·235	59·13	1720	0·108	276·69
195	0·612	8·203	730	0·232	60·54	1740	0·107	282·60
200	0·603	8·473	740	0·229	61·96	1760	0·106	288·58
205	0·594	8·748	750	0·227	63·39	1780	0·105	294·62
210	0·585	9·026	760	0·224	64·84	1800	0·104	300·72

One of these factors must be assumed. It is most common to assume the
pressure drop by settling what you want the final pressure to be. If you do this
the tables will give you the velocity.

It is also possible to assume the velocity. In this case, the tables will give you
the pressure drop.

The practice

Figure 203 shows a typical steam layout for which it is required to find the
correct pipe sizes. Steam is available at S at 800 kPa. It must be available at A,
B, C, D and E at a pressure of not less than 750 kPa.

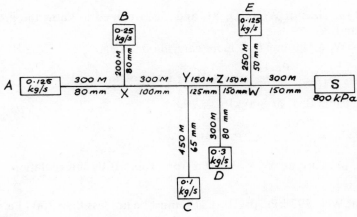

Figure 203

Consider first the least favoured circuit S to A.

$p_1 = 800\ \text{kPa}$ $\therefore P_1 = 70.80$ (Table B)

$p_2 = 750\ \text{kPa}$ $\therefore P_2 = 63.39$

$$\therefore F = \frac{P_1 - P_2}{L} = \frac{70.80 - 63.39}{1200} = 0.006$$

This means that 0.006 is the constant factor of pressure drop per unit length
throughout the circuit SA.

To find the pipe size between X and A, we look down the left hand column of
Table A for the factor F of 0.006 and read across to the right to see that a 65 mm
($2\frac{1}{2}''$) pipe is too small and we should choose an 80 mm (3″) pipe to carry the load
of 0.125 kg/s. This is the pipe size from A to X at which point conditions alter.

It is also noted from Table A that the velocity factor (Y) for an 80 mm (3″)
pipe carrying 0.125 kg/s is 27.56. This gives a true velocity of
$27.56 \times 0.23 = 6.3$ m/s (0.23 m³/kg is the specific volume of steam at 750 kPa).

This is well within our recommended limits and we can now proceed with the pipe sizing.

Consider XY $F = 0.006$, load = 0.375 kg/s
                    From Table A, size = 100 mm (4″)

Consider YZ $F = 0.006$, load = 0.475 kg/s
                    From Table A, size = 125 mm (5″)

Consider ZW $F = 0.006$, load = 0.775 kg/s
                    From Table A, size = 150 mm (6″)

Consider WS $F = 0.006$, load = 0.9 kg/s
                    From Table A, size = 150 mm (6″)

To find the sizes of WE, ZD, YC and XB, we need to know the pressures at W, Z, Y and X.

Consider SW, a 150 mm (6″) main carrying 0.9 kg/s.

From Table A, $F = \dfrac{P_1 - P_2}{L} = 0.0038$ by interpolation,

and from Table B, P_1 at 800 kPa = 70.80

$\therefore \dfrac{70.80 - P_2}{300} = 0.0038$ and $P_2 = 69.66$

$\therefore P_2$ (i.e. pressure at W) = 792 kPa from Table B by interpolation.

Consider WE
Pressure at W = 792 kPa, pressure at E must be not less than 750 kPa. Length is 250 m.

$\therefore$ (From Table B) $\dfrac{P_1 - P_2}{L} = F = \dfrac{69.66 - 63.39}{250} = 0.0251$

From Table A, $F = 0.0251$, load = 0.125 kg/s
$\therefore$ size = 50 mm (2″)

Consider WZ, a 150 mm (6″) main carrying 0.775 kg/s.

From Table A, $F = \dfrac{P_1 - P_2}{L} = 0.0030$ and $P_1 = 69.66$

$\therefore \dfrac{69.66 - P_2}{150} = 0.0030$ and $P_2 = 69.21$

$\therefore P_2$ (i.e. pressure at Z) = 790 kPa from Table B.

Consider ZD
Pressure at Z = 790 kPa, pressure at D must be not less than 750 kPa. Length is 300 m.

$$\therefore \frac{P_1 - P_2}{L} = F = \frac{69.21 - 63.39}{300} = 0.0194$$

From Table A, $F = 0.0194$, load $= 0.3$ kg/s
$\therefore$ size $= 80$ mm (3″)

Consider ZY, a 125 mm (5″) main carrying 0.475 kg/s

From Table A, $F = \dfrac{P_1 - P_2}{L} = 0.0030$

$$\therefore \frac{69.21 - P_2}{150} = 0.0030 \text{ and } P_2 = 68.76$$
$\therefore P_2$ (i.e. pressure at Y) $= 787$ kPa.

Consider YC
Pressure at Y $= 787$ kPa, pressure at C must be not less than 750 kPa. Length is 450 m.

$$\therefore \frac{P_1 - P_2}{L} = F = \frac{68.76 - 63.39}{450} = 0.0119$$

From Table A, $F = 0.0119$, load $= 0.1$ kg/s
$\therefore$ size $= 65$ mm ($2\frac{1}{2}$″)

Consider YX, a 100 mm (4″) main carrying 0.375 kg/s

From Table A, $F = \dfrac{P_1 - P_2}{L} = 0.0055$

$$\therefore \frac{68.76 - P_2}{300} = 0.0055 \text{ and } P_2 = 67.11$$

$\therefore P_2$ (i.e. pressure at X) $= 775$ kPa.

Consider XB
Pressure at X $= 775$ kPa, pressure at B must be not less than 750 kPa. Length is 200 m.

$$\therefore \frac{P_1 - P_2}{L} = F = \frac{67.11 - 63.39}{200} = 0.0186$$

From Table A, $F = 0.0186$, load $= 0.25$ kg/s
$\therefore$ size $= 80$ mm (3″)

It should be noted that the lengths given have been taken as effective lengths after allowing for bends and fittings. Because all the lengths are at least 100 m, a 10 % allowance has been made.

Appendix 2 Sizing condensate return pipes

The capacity of condensate pipes, like all other pipes carrying fluids, depends on the difference in pressure at the two ends. It is not correct to treat a condensate pipe as one carrying hot water only – it also has to discharge air and flash steam. Neither is it correct to size the pipe as you would a steam pipe or an air pipe. The size of a condensate pipe should be somewhere between these two extremes, but nobody can tell where.

Nevertheless, condensate pipes must be sized somehow. Some engineers make the condensate pipe one size smaller than the steam pipe. This gives pipes that are generally oversized and therefore expensive. The method which follows has at least a slight justification in theory; it has been tried out over a period of years and found satisfactory and it does not give pipe sizes which are much too large.

The amount of air to be discharged is greatest when the plant is starting up and this is followed by the heaviest discharge of condensate which is cool to start with so there is not much flash steam. Then, as the plant heats up, the amount of condensate falls off but the quantity of flash reaches its maximum. If, therefore, the pipe is sized on the heavy starting load of condensate it will only be partly full of water when normal running conditions are reached and room will be available for the flash steam. It will also easily handle the initial discharge of air.

All pipe lines should have a fall, preferably in the direction of flow. If the fall in a water pipe is graded so that the fall per metre is equal to or greater than the head lost in friction per metre, then the water will flow freely, without needing pressure to push it along – i.e. without causing a back pressure.

If, however, the pipe line is horizontal, the back pressure set up to cause flow will be equal to the loss of head in friction per metre multiplied by the length of the pipe.

If the pipe *must* rise, then a pressure must be available to push the water up and this pressure (which is back pressure on the trap) will equal the head of the lift plus the frictional head per metre × the length of the pipe.

Now please look at Table C. It gives you

(1) The loss of head in Pascals due to the friction of a certain flow of water passing along one metre of pipe of a certain size.
(2) The equivalent fall in the pipe necessary to balance this frictional loss.
(3) The various rates of flow and sizes of pipe causing this frictional loss.

Table C Condensate pipe sizing

Column 1 frictional resistance Pa/m	Column 2 pipe fall to overcome pipe friction	Column 3 nominal pipe sizes										
		15 mm (½″)	20 mm (¾″)	25 mm (1″)	32 mm (1¼″)	40 mm (1½″)	50 mm (2″)	65 mm (2½″)	80 mm (3″)	100 mm (4″)	125 mm (5″)	150 mm (6″)
		kg. of water per second										
20	10 mm in 4.8 m	0.014	0.040	0.100	0.179	0.296	0.649	1.11	1.89	3.81	7.56	11.8
30	10 mm in 3.2 m	0.018	0.053	0.123	0.219	0.359	0.760	1.39	2.28	4.91	9.20	14.7
40	10 mm in 2.4 m	0.022	0.064	0.140	0.252	0.413	0.895	1.63	2.65	5.71	10.3	16.9
50	10 mm in 2.0 m	0.025	0.071	0.155	0.285	0.460	0.995	1.81	2.96	6.33	11.6	18.8
60	10 mm in 1.6 m	0.027	0.079	0.174	0.312	0.500	1.09	1.99	3.31	7.06	12.8	21.0
70	10 mm in 1.4 m	0.030	0.086	0.184	0.340	0.548	1.18	2.18	3.59	7.81	14.0	22.8
80	10 mm in 1.2 m	0.032	0.092	0.202	0.365	0.600	1.29	2.36	3.87	8.44	15.1	25.2
90	10 mm in 1.1 m	0.034	0.098	0.209	0.392	0.630	1.38	2.43	4.06	8.88	15.6	27.1
100	10 mm in 1.0 m	0.036	0.103	0.222	0.416	0.670	1.46	2.51	4.32	9.39	16.9	28.4
125	10 mm in 0.8 m	0.040	0.117	0.252	0.466	0.756	1.64	2.99	4.88	10.5	19.1	31.8
150	10 mm in 0.7 m	0.045	0.130	0.282	0.517	0.838	1.80	3.31	5.39	11.6	21.0	34.9
175	10 mm in 0.6 m	0.048	0.142	0.309	0.561	0.907	1.92	3.59	5.83	12.6	22.9	37.8
200	10 mm in 0.5 m	0.052	0.154	0.331	0.600	0.974	2.10	3.84	6.27	13.5	24.3	40.6
225	10 mm in 0.45 m	0.055	0.161	0.350	0.636	1.04	2.25	4.10	6.82	14.4	26.1	42.8
250	10 mm in 0.4 m	0.058	0.172	0.368	0.674	1.10	2.38	4.35	7.18	15.3	27.3	45.4
275	10 mm in 0.35 m	0.060	0.181	0.388	0.712	1.16	2.50	4.57	7.50	16.2	29.2	47.9
300	10 mm in 0.3 m	0.063	0.190	0.410	0.743	1.21	2.62	4.79	7.81	17.1	30.6	50.1

Examples

These show the method of applying Table C for the determination of condensate pipe sizes:

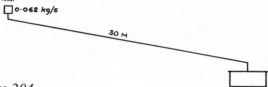

Example 1: Figure 204

A trap discharges 0.062 kg/s of condensate which has to be carried 30 m to the feed tank. What size pipe is needed?

From Table C, a 15 mm ($\frac{1}{2}''$) pipe will do if you have available a fall of 10 mm in 0.3 m, which is 1 m over the length.

A 20 mm ($\frac{3}{4}''$) pipe needs a fall of 10 mm in 2.4 m or 0.13 m over the length.

Suppose that you want to use a 15 mm ($\frac{1}{2}''$) pipe and have only a fall of 0.25 m available. This means that the other 0.75 m of frictional head must be provided for by a back pressure at the trap of 0.75 m of water – approximately 7.4 kPa.

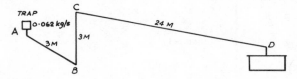

Example 2: Figure 205

A trap discharges 0.062 kg/s of condensate which has to be carried 30 m to the feed tank, but be lifted 3 m at one point. What size pipe is needed?

Well, first of all there must be available at the trap a back pressure equal to 3 m of water to overcome the lift (= 29.6 kPa).

Apart from this the problem is just the same as before. If a fall at the rate of 10 mm in 0.3 m can be arranged in AB and CD, then a 15 mm ($\frac{1}{2}''$) pipe will pass the quantity. If this fall is not available, either a 20 mm ($\frac{3}{4}''$) pipe must be used or you must put up with increased back pressure at the trap to make up the difference between the 1 m wanted and what is available.

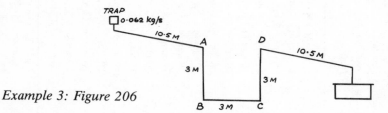

Example 3: Figure 206

This is the same set of facts, i.e. 0.062 kg/s of condensate to be carried a total of 30 m, but the condensate has to pass under an alleyway en route.

It is suggested that no water can flow away from D until the whole of ABCD is solid water. If you agree with this you must then agree that here, at last, is an example of a piece of pipe running full.

The 3 m lift CD will be balanced out by the 3 m fall AB. All that is required to cause a flow from D at the required rate is a head equal to the frictional loss in ABCD. In other words the point A should be higher than the point D by the frictional head lost between the two points.

If we are using the 15 mm ($\frac{1}{2}''$) pipe, this, you may remember, is 10 mm in 0.3 m or $\dfrac{0.01}{0.3} \times 9 = 0.3$ m.

If we are using a 20 mm ($\frac{3}{4}''$) pipe it will be 10 mm in 2.4 m or $\dfrac{0.01}{2.4} \times 9 = 0.04$ m.

Maybe, for practical reasons, A and D must be at the same level. If this is so, the back pressure on the trap will be increased by 3 kPa using the 15 mm ($\frac{1}{2}''$) pipe or 0.4 kPa using the 20 mm ($\frac{3}{4}''$) pipe.

One point arises in this layout which is worth noting. There should be some means of getting rid of the gases which might be trapped at A. Either put a vent at a A (high enough to take care of the back pressure), or couple A to D by an overhead line.

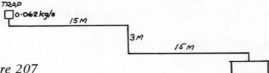

Example 4: Figure 207

Here the facts are as before, but there is a vertical drop of 3 m in the pipe. This problem is completely insoluble from the theoretical standpoint.

What is the effect of that 3 m fall? If it were a system with the pipes running full of water, that fall would represent a gain of the full 3 m in the head available to cause flow. But these pipes are *not* full all the time (if ever).

Does that 3 m fall exert a suction pull on the upper pipe, thus causing flow?

If the pipes were full it certainly would. When the pipes are not full, there will be some suction effect excited through the gases present, but it is impossible to tell how much.

This is a practical suggestion. First of all, neglect the vertical fall. In the present example we know that a 15 mm ($\frac{1}{2}''$) pipe will be big enough to pass 0.062 kg/s if the fall is 10 mm in 0.3 m, but a 20 mm ($\frac{3}{4}''$) pipe is needed if this fall cannot be arranged or a back pressure tolerated.

Let us now say that the vertical fall will make enough difference to make a 15 mm ($\frac{1}{2}''$) pipe amply big enough and cause no back pressure, even if you cannot get the full fall of 1 m over the whole length.

In other words, when you have this problem of the vertical fall in a condensate pipe, as a first approximation, neglect the effect of it; but when you finally come to make your pipe choice remember that you have a margin in hand and act accordingly.

Appendix 3 Condensation rates

The rate at which steam will condense on any surface depends upon so many factors that it is quite impossible to calculate condensation rates with any degree of certainty. The factors influencing heat transmission are the area of the surface, the nature of the surface, the material, the presence of stagnant films on both sides, the velocity over the surface, the temperature head and the wettability of the surface.

It is obvious that no set of tables can take care of all these variables. On the other hand some indication of the probable rate of condensate formation is needed if a steam trap is to be correctly sized.

On existing plant, the most accurate method is to weigh the condensate formed at intervals over a period.

If the plant is new, the makers can often tell you what is the rated steam consumption.

If both of these methods fail, the tables which follow may be helpful as an approximate guide.

Steam mains

(a) Warming-up rate

$$Q = \frac{W \times (T - t) \times 0.49}{h_{f_g} \times m \times 60}$$

where Q = rate of condensation in kg/s
$\quad W$ = total weight of pipe including flanges and fittings in kg
$\quad T$ = steam temperature in °C
$\quad t$ = initial temperature in °C
$\quad 0.49$ = Specific heat capacity of steel in kJ/kg °C
$\quad h_{f_g}$ = Specific enthalpy of evaporation of steam at the working pressure in kJ/kg.
$\quad m$ = time taken in warming up in minutes

Table D gives approximate weights of steel pipes and flanges. If the main contains stop valves or other fittings these should be taken into account when calculating the total weight.

Table D   Weights of steel pipes and flanges

nominal pipe size	approx. weight of 1 m of steel pipe in kg	approximate weight of a pair of flanges including bolts and nuts in kg	
		BS 4504 NP. 16	BS 4504 NP. 25/40
15 mm ($\frac{1}{2}''$)	1.5	1.5	1.8
20 mm ($\frac{3}{4}''$)	2.0	2.4	2.8
25 mm (1″)	3.0	3.1	3.4
32 mm ($1\frac{1}{4}''$)	3.8	3.3	3.8
40 mm ($1\frac{1}{2}''$)	4.5	3.8	4.4
50 mm (2″)	6.2	5.5	6.5
65 mm ($2\frac{1}{2}''$)	8.0	6.5	9.5
80 mm (3″)	10.0	8.5	10.5
100 mm (4″)	14.5	9.5	14.5
125 mm (5″)	17.8	14.0	18.5
150 mm (6″)	20.0	18.5	25.0

Because a steam main may be warmed-up more quickly than expected the calculated rate of condensation should be multiplied by a factor of 3 when sizing the steam traps.

Example

Find the rate of condensation in warming up 100 metres of 100 mm (4″) steel main which includes 20 flanged joints to BS 4504 NP.25. The initial temperature is 10 °C and the steam pressure 1700 kPa. Time taken is 30 minutes.

W (from Table D) = 14.5 × 100 + 14.5 × 20 = 1740 kg
T (from Table H) = 207 °C

$t = 10$ °C
h_{f_g} (from Table H) = 1912 kJ/kg

$m = 30$ minutes

$$Q = \frac{1740 \times (207 - 10) \times 0.49}{1912 \times 30 \times 60}$$

= 0.049 kg/s

This rate of condensation should now be multiplied by a factor of 3 and divided by the total number of traps fitted to arrive at the trap capacity.

(b) Radiation losses

Table E gives the heat losses from bare steel piping.

Table E Heat emission (W/m run) from bare horizontal steel pipes freely exposed in still air

temperature difference between surface and surroundings in °C

nominal pipe size	50	55	60	65	70	80	90	100	120	140	160	180	200	220
10 mm ($\frac{3}{8}''$)	41	46	50	55	60	70	82	95	120	160	190	230	270	310
15 mm ($\frac{1}{2}''$)	53	59	66	73	80	96	110	130	170	200	240	290	340	400
20 mm ($\frac{3}{4}''$)	62	70	78	87	95	110	130	150	200	250	300	350	420	480
25 mm (1″)	78	88	98	110	120	140	160	190	240	300	370	430	510	590
32 mm ($1\frac{1}{4}''$)	93	110	120	130	150	170	200	230	300	370	450	540	630	730
40 mm ($1\frac{1}{2}''$)	105	120	130	150	160	190	230	260	330	410	510	600	710	830
50 mm (2″)	130	150	170	180	200	240	270	320	410	500	620	740	860	1000
65 mm ($2\frac{1}{2}''$)	160	180	200	220	240	290	330	390	500	610	750	900	1100	1300
80 mm (3″)	180	210	230	250	280	330	380	450	580	710	900	1100	1300	1500
100 mm (4″)	230	260	290	310	350	410	480	550	710	900	1100	1300	1500	1800
125 mm (5″)	270	310	350	380	420	490	580	660	850	1100	1300	1600	1900	2100
150 mm (6″)	320	350	400	440	480	570	660	770	1000	1200	1500	1800	2100	2500

If the piping is lagged the rate of condensation will be reduced by 75 % and it would be safe to divide the bare pipe rate by 4.

To find the rate of condensation, find the steam temperature at the working pressure from Steam tables and subtract from this the air temperature in the room = A.

From Table E find the watts per metre run of piping of the size used at the temperature difference found above = B.

From Steam tables (Table H) find the Specific enthalpy of evaporation of steam at the working pressure = C.

$$\text{Rate of condensation in kg/s} = \frac{B \times \text{length of pipe in metres}}{1000 \times C}$$

Example

Find the rate of condensation in 30 m of 80 mm (3″) bare steel piping working at 700 kPa. Air temperature 10 °C.

A = 170.5 − 10 = 160.5 °C
B = 900 W/m
C = 2048 kJ/kg

$$\text{Rate of condensation} = \frac{900 \times 30}{1000 \times 2048} = 0.013 \text{ kg/s}$$

Lagging would reduce this to about $\frac{1}{4}$, and the rate of condensation would be $\frac{0.013}{4} = 0.003$ kg/s.

Heating pipes

Table E should be used to find the rate of condensation in heating pipes. The figures given are for fairly still air. When air is blown over pipe coils by a fan the rate of condensation is increased.

The following factors should be used when the air velocity is known:

velocity of air passing over pipe surface in m/s	multiplying co-efficient factor
still air	1
1.5	1.4
3	2.2
6	3.2
9	4.0
15	5.2

Where pipes are assembled into horizontal coils with several rows of pipes one above the other and without any means of blowing air over the pipes they become less efficient as the number of pipes is increased.

The following figures give approximately the reduction in efficiency according to the number of rows high:

pipes high	1	2	3	4	5	6	7	8	9	10
efficiency	1.00	.96	.91	.86	.82	.78	.74	.70	.67	.63

Vertical pipes are also less efficient than horizontal pipes and the following figures should be used to correct Table E:

pipe size	10 mm $(\frac{3}{8}'')$	15 mm $(\frac{1}{2}'')$	20 mm $(\frac{3}{4}'')$	25 mm $(1'')$	32 mm $(1\frac{1}{4}'')$	40 mm $(1\frac{1}{2}'')$
multiplying factor	0.74	0.76	0.8	0.82	0.84	0.86

pipe size	50 mm $(2'')$	65 mm $(2\frac{1}{2}'')$	80 mm $(3'')$	100 mm $(4'')$	125 mm $(5'')$	150 mm $(6'')$
multiplying factor	0.88	0.91	0.93	0.95	0.97	1

Unit heaters and heater batteries

Heater manufacturers give the output of their units in kW. From this the condensation rate can be calculated by dividing the kW output by the Specific enthalpy of evaporation of steam at the working pressure.

Thus a 50 kW heater working at 700 kPa will condense:

$$\frac{50}{2048} = 0.024 \text{ kg/s}$$

When the volume of air being heated by an air heater, the temperature rise and the steam pressure are known, the approximate rate of condensation can be calculated from the following formula:

$$Q = \frac{V \times t \times Sp}{h_{f_g}}$$

where Q = rate of condensation in kg/s
V = volume of air heated in m³/s
t = temperature rise in °C
Sp = Specific heat capacity of air at constant pressure = 1.34 kJ/m³ °C
h_{f_g} = Specific enthalpy of evaporation of steam at the working pressure

A heater battery with a capacity of 2 m³/s of air raises the temperature of this air from 15 °C to 80 °C with steam at 700 kPa. Find the rate of condensation.

$$V = 2 \text{ m}^3/\text{s}$$
$$t = 80 - 15 \text{ °C} = 65 \text{ °C}$$
$$Sp = 1.34 \text{ kJ/m}^3 \text{ °C}$$
$$h_{f_g} = 2048 \text{ kJ/kg}$$
$$\therefore Q = \frac{2 \times 65 \times 1.34}{2048}$$
$$= 0.085 \text{ kg/s}$$

Heating calorifiers

Makers usually rate their calorifiers in kW output and from this rating the condensation can be calculated as for unit heaters and heater batteries. However this can be misleading, because calorifiers are often too large for the systems they are asked to serve. The design heat load calculations for the building will have included safety factors and the calorifier itself will have been chosen from a standard range, with the probability that its capacity will be somewhat larger than the design figure.

An idea of the actual load at any time can sometimes be obtained if the flow and return temperatures in the heating system and the pumping rate are known. But take care because the pump duty given on the plate attached to the pump will probably refer to a pressure head on the discharge side which may or may not obtain in practice.

Another way of estimating the load is to look at the buildings being heated. Calculations of heating load can be complicated, involving such factors as the number of air changes and heat transfer rates through cavity walls, windows and roofs. However, a reasonable estimate can usually be obtained by taking the total volume of the building and simply allowing 112 kJ/m³. This will give a running load when the outside temperature is around −1 °C.

The best way of obtaining the steam consumption is to measure the weight of condensate being discharged from the trap draining the calorifier. At the same time the ambient conditions should be noted so that the maximum steam consumption can be calculated.

Hot water storage calorifiers

Hot water storage calorifiers are designed to raise the temperature of the whole of the contents from cold to the storage temperature in a specified period of time. The average rate at which steam is condensed during the heating up period can be calculated by means of the following formula:

$$Q = \frac{W \times Sp \times t}{h_{f_g} \times H \times 3600}$$

Where Q = rate of condensation in kg/s
$\quad\quad W$ = weight of water heated in kg
$\quad\quad Sp$ = Specific heat capacity of water = 4.186 kJ/kg °C
$\quad\quad t$ = temperature rise in °C
$\quad\quad h_{f_g}$ = Specific enthalpy of evaporation of steam at the working pressure
$\quad\quad H$ = recovery time in hours

A hot water storage calorifier having a capacity of 2000 litres has to raise the temperature of the contents from 10 °C to 60 °C in 2 hours using steam at 800 kPa gauge pressure.

In this case W = 2000 kg since 1 litre of water weighs 1 kg
$\quad\quad\quad Sp$ = 4.186 kJ/kg °C
$\quad\quad\quad t$ = 60 – 10 °C = 50 °C
$\quad\quad\quad h_{f_g}$ = 2031 kJ/kg
$\quad\quad\quad H$ = 2 hours

$$Q = \frac{2000 \times 4.186 \times 50}{2031 \times 2 \times 3600}$$

$$= 0.029 \text{ kg/s}$$

This consumption is the figure to use as a basis for sizing the control valve and steam trap. As in the case of heating calorifiers, there is no need to use a safety factor when sizing the control valve but a factor of 2 should be used when determining the size of the steam trap because of the high pressure drop which will occur at the start of each recovery period.

Submerged heating coils

It is very common for liquids in tanks and vats to be heated by means of submerged steam coils.

The heat output from a submerged coil can be calculated from the following formula:

$$Q = UA \, (T_2 - T_1)$$

Where Q = heat output from coil in W
$\quad\quad U$ = overall heat transfer coefficient from the steam in the coil to the liquid being heated in W/m² °C
$\quad\quad A$ = surface area of heating coil in m²
$\quad\quad T_2$ = mean temperature of heating surface in °C
$\quad\quad T_1$ = mean temperature of liquid being heated in °C

The steam consumption of the coil in kg/s can readily be found by dividing Q in kW by the Specific enthalpy of evaporation (h_{f_g}) of the steam at the working pressure in kJ/kg.

There are, however, a number of variables to be considered. The overall heat transfer coefficient varies with temperature head, fouling of the inside and outside surfaces of the coil, the material from which the coil is made, the viscosity of the liquid being heated and its velocity across the heating surface.

Table F lists approximate overall heat transfer coefficients for some typical fluids.

Because overall heat transfer is largely governed by the resistant films which occur on both sides of the heating surface (see chapter 4, page 74), the thermal conductivity of the coil itself is generally unimportant and Table F can be used for coils made from steel, brass or copper.

If the coil is a long one, the pressure drop can become significant and, when calculating the mean temperature of the heating surface (T_2), an average steam pressure of about 75 % of the nominal inlet pressure should be used. For very long coils of small bore pipe a figure as low as 40 % may have to be used.

The temperature difference $T_2 - T_1$ should in theory be the logarithmic mean. However, with a steam heated coil in which the primary medium is at a constant temperature, it is usually sufficiently accurate to use the arithmetic mean temperature difference

Table G shows the surface areas of 1 metre lengths of steel pipes of various diameters.

Example 1

Find the steam consumption of a water heating coil comprising 100 m of 40 mm ($1\frac{1}{2}''$) steel tube which is raising the temperature of the water from 10 °C to 80 °C by natural convection. Steam pressure 350 kPa.

U (from Table F) = 570 W/m^2°C
A_1 (from Table G) = 100 × 0.152 = 15.2 m^2
T_2 = 140°C (based on a mean pressure of about 75 % of 350 kPa = 260 kPa)
$$T_1 = \frac{10 + 80}{2} = 45°C$$

Q = 570 × 15.2 × (140 − 45)
    = 823 kW

h_{f_g} of steam at 260 kPa = 2145 kJ/kg (from Table H)

$$\therefore \text{ Steam consumption} = \frac{823}{2145}$$
$$= 0.384 \text{ kg/s}$$

Example 2

Find the length of 25 mm (1″) steel pipe in one continuous coil, required to raise the temperature of 450 litres of water from 5 °C to 50 °C in 20 minutes with steam at 280 kPa. The water is pumped across the coil so that the heat transfer is by forced convection.

First find the heat required which = weight of water × Specific heat capacity × temperature rise

$$= 450 \times 4.186 \times 45$$
$$= 84\ 767 \text{ kJ}$$

This has to be supplied in 20 minutes, so the heat output from the coil (Q)

$$= \frac{84\ 767}{20 \times 60} = 70.6 \text{ kW}$$

So in our formula $Q = 70\ 600$ W

$$U = 1140 \text{ W/m}^2\ °C$$
$$A = \text{to be found}$$
$$T_2 = 135\ °C \text{ (saturated steam temperature at } 0.75 \times 280$$
$$= 210 \text{ kPa)}$$
$$T_1 = \frac{5 + 50}{2} = 22.5\ °C$$

$$\therefore 70\ 600 = 1140 \times A \times (135 - 22.5)$$

$$\therefore A = \frac{70\ 600}{1140 \times 112.5} = 0.55 \text{ m}^2$$

Length of 25 mm (1″) coil at 0.106 m² per metre $= \dfrac{0.55}{0.106} = 5.2$ m.

Table F Approximate overall heat transfer co-efficients for pipe coils submerged in various fluids

fluid	W/m² °C
water (natural convection using steam at 130 to 300 kPa)	570
water (natural convection using steam at 550 to 850 kPa)	1140
water (forced convection using steam at 130 to 300 kPa)	1140
water (forced convection using steam at 550 to 850 kPa)	1700
light oils (200 seconds Redwood at 38 °C)(natural convection)	170
light oils (200 seconds Redwood at 38 °C)(forced convection)	570
medium oils (1000 seconds Redwood at 38 °C)(forced convection)	340
heavy oils (3500 seconds Redwood at 38 °C)(natural convection)	85–113
heavy oils (3500 seconds Redwood at 38 °C)(forced convection)	170
fats (50 000 seconds Redwood at 38 °C)(natural convection)[1]	28–57
fats (50 000 seconds Redwood at 38 °C)(forced convection)[1]	57
molasses (10 000 seconds Redwood at 38 °C)(forced convection)[2]	85

1. Some substances such as margarine and tallow are solid at normal ambient temperatures but have quite a low viscosity when molten.
2. Commercially, molasses frequently contains water and the viscosity is then much lower.

Table G   Surface areas of steel pipes

nominal bore	surface (m²) per metre length
10 mm (³/₈″)	0.054
15 mm (½″)	0.067
20 mm (¾″)	0.085
25 mm (1″)	0.106
32 mm (1¼″)	0.134
40 mm (1½″)	0.152
50 mm (2″)	0.189
65 mm (2½″)	0.239
80 mm (3″)	0.279
100 mm (4″)	0.358
125 mm (5″)	0.438
150 mm (6″)	0.518

Drying machines

It is sometimes impossible to obtain reliable figures for the condensation rates of steam heated machines. In such cases the following approximate formula will be found helpful. It is, of course, only approximate.

$$C = \frac{K}{L} \left[(W - D) \times 2560 + 1.26 \times D \times (T - t) \right]$$

where C = condensation rate in kg/s
W = wet weight of material being dried in kg/s
D = dry weight of material being dried in kg/s
T = temperature of material leaving dryer in °C
t = temperature of material entering dryer in °C
L = Specific enthalpy of evaporation of steam at the working pressure in kJ/kg
K = 1.0 for contact dryers without steam heated rolls
1.5 for contact dryers with steam heated rolls
2.0 for non-circulating air dryers

Appendix 4 Steam tables

Table H

absolute pressure		temperature in °C	Specific enthalpy			Specific volume steam
in kPa	in Bar		water (h_f) (Sensible heat) in kJ/kg	evaporation (h_{f_g}) (Latent heat) in kJ/kg	steam (h_g) (Total heat) in kJ/kg	m^3/kg
10.0	0.1	45.8	192	2393	2585	14.67
20.0	0.2	60.1	251	2358	2609	7.65
30.0	0.3	69.1	289	2336	2625	5.23
40.0	0.4	75.9	318	2319	2637	3.99
50.0	0.5	81.3	340	2305	2645	3.24
60.0	0.6	85.9	360	2294	2654	2.73
70.0	0.7	90.0	377	2283	2660	2.37
80.0	0.8	93.5	392	2274	2666	2.09
90.0	0.9	96.7	405	2266	2671	1.87
gauge pressure						
0	0	100.0	419	2257	2676	1.67
10	0.1	102.7	430	2250	2680	1.53
20	0.2	105.1	441	2243	2684	1.41
30	0.3	107.4	450	2237	2687	1.31
40	0.4	109.6	460	2231	2691	1.23
50	0.5	111.6	468	2226	2694	1.15
60	0.6	113.6	476	2220	2696	1.08
70	0.7	115.4	484	2215	2699	1.02
80	0.8	117.1	492	2211	2703	0.97
90	0.9	118.8	499	2207	2706	0.92
100	1.0	120.4	506	2201	2707	0.88
110	1.1	122.0	512	2197	2709	0.84
120	1.2	123.5	519	2193	2712	0.81
130	1.3	124.9	525	2189	2714	0.77
140	1.4	126.3	531	2185	2716	0.74
150	1.5	127.6	536	2181	2717	0.71
160	1.6	128.9	542	2177	2719	0.69
170	1.7	130.1	547	2174	2721	0.67
180	1.8	131.4	552	2170	2722	0.64
190	1.9	132.5	557	2167	2724	0.62
200	2.0	133.7	562	2163	2725	0.60
210	2.1	134.8	567	2160	2727	0.59
220	2.2	135.9	572	2157	2729	0.57
230	2.3	137.0	576	2154	2730	0.55
240	2.4	138.0	581	2151	2732	0.54
250	2.5	139.0	585	2148	2733	0.52
260	2.6	140.0	589	2145	2734	0.51
270	2.7	141.0	593	2142	2735	0.50

gauge pressure		temperature in °C	Specific enthalpy			Specific volume steam
in kPa	in Bar		water (h_f) (Sensible heat) in kJ/kg	evaporation (h_{fg}) (Latent heat) in kJ/kg	steam (h_g) (Total heat) in kJ/kg	m^3/kg
280	2.8	141.9	597	2139	2736	0.48
290	2.9	142.9	601	2136	2737	0.47
300	3.0	143.8	605	2133	2738	0.46
310	3.1	144.7	609	2131	2740	0.45
320	3.2	145.5	613	2128	2741	0.44
330	3.3	146.4	616	2126	2742	0.43
340	3.4	147.2	620	2123	2743	0.42
350	3.5	148.0	624	2120	2744	0.41
360	3.6	148.9	627	2118	2745	0.41
370	3.7	149.6	631	2115	2746	0.40
380	3.8	150.4	634	2113	2747	0.39
390	3.9	151.2	637	2111	2748	0.38
400	4.0	152.0	641	2108	2749	0.37
410	4.1	152.7	644	2106	2750	0.37
420	4.2	153.4	647	2104	2751	0.36
430	4.3	154.1	650	2101	2751	0.36
440	4.4	154.8	653	2099	2752	0.35
450	4.5	155.6	656	2097	2753	0.34
460	4.6	156.2	659	2095	2754	0.34
470	4.7	156.9	662	2092	2754	0.33
480	4.8	157.6	665	2090	2755	0.33
490	4.9	158.3	668	2088	2756	0.32
500	5.0	158.9	671	2086	2757	0.32
510	5.1	159.6	674	2084	2758	0.31
520	5.2	160.2	677	2082	2759	0.31
530	5.3	160.8	679	2080	2759	0.30
540	5.4	161.5	682	2078	2760	0.30
550	5.5	162.1	685	2076	2761	0.29
560	5.6	162.7	687	2074	2761	0.29
570	5.7	163.3	690	2072	2762	0.28
580	5.8	163.9	692	2070	2762	0.28
590	5.9	164.5	695	2068	2763	0.28
600	6.0	165.0	698	2066	2764	0.27
610	6.1	165.6	700	2064	2764	0.27
620	6.2	166.2	703	2062	2765	0.27
630	6.3	166.7	705	2060	2765	0.26
640	6.4	167.3	707	2059	2766	0.26
650	6.5	167.8	710	2057	2767	0.26
660	6.6	168.4	712	2055	2767	0.25
670	6.7	168.9	715	2053	2768	0.25
680	6.8	169.4	717	2051	2768	0.25
690	6.9	170.0	719	2050	2769	0.24
700	7.0	170.5	721	2048	2769	0.24
710	7.1	171.0	724	2046	2770	0.24
720	7.2	171.5	726	2044	2770	0.24
730	7.3	172.0	728	2043	2771	0.23
740	7.4	172.5	730	2041	2771	0.23
750	7.5	173.0	733	2039	2772	0.23
760	7.6	173.5	735	2038	2773	0.22
770	7.7	174.0	737	2036	2773	0.22
780	7.8	174.5	739	2034	2773	0.22
790	7.9	174.9	741	2033	2774	0.22
800	8.0	175.4	743	2031	2774	0.22

| gauge pressure | | temperature in °C | Specific enthalpy | | | Specific volume steam |
in kPa	in Bar		water (h_f) (Sensible heat) in kJ/kg	evaporation (h_{f_g}) (Latent heat) in kJ/kg	steam (h_g) (Total heat) in kJ/kg	m^3/kg
810	8.1	175.9	745	2029	2774	0.21
820	8.2	176.4	747	2028	2775	0.21
830	8.3	176.8	749	2026	2775	0.21
840	8.4	177.3	751	2025	2776	0.21
850	8.5	177.8	753	2023	2776	0.20
860	8.6	178.2	755	2021	2776	0.20
870	8.7	178.6	757	2020	2777	0.20
880	8.8	179.1	759	2018	2777	0.20
890	8.9	179.5	761	2017	2778	0.20
900	9.0	180.0	763	2015	2778	0.19
910	9.1	180.4	765	2014	2779	0.19
920	9.2	180.8	767	2012	2779	0.19
930	9.3	181.3	769	2011	2780	0.19
940	9.4	181.7	771	2009	2780	0.19
950	9.5	182.1	773	2007	2780	0.19
960	9.6	182.5	774	2006	2780	0.18
970	9.7	182.9	776	2005	2781	0.18
980	9.8	183.3	778	2003	2781	0.18
990	9.9	183.7	780	2002	2782	0.18
1000	10.0	184.1	782	2000	2782	0.18
1020	10.2	184.9	785	1997	2782	0.17
1040	10.4	185.7	789	1994	2783	0.17
1060	10.6	186.5	792	1992	2784	0.17
1080	10.8	187.3	796	1989	2785	0.17
1100	11.0	188.0	799	1986	2785	0.16
1120	11.2	188.8	802	1983	2785	0.16
1140	11.4	189.5	806	1981	2787	0.16
1160	11.6	190.2	809	1978	2787	0.16
1180	11.8	190.8	812	1975	2787	0.15
1200	12.0	191.7	815	1973	2788	0.15
1220	12.2	192.4	818	1970	2788	0.15
1240	12.4	193.1	821	1967	2788	0.15
1260	12.6	193.8	825	1965	2790	0.15
1280	12.8	194.4	828	1962	2790	0.14
1300	13.0	195.1	830	1960	2790	0.14
1320	13.2	195.8	833	1957	2790	0.14
1340	13.4	196.4	836	1955	2791	0.14
1360	13.6	197.1	839	1952	2791	0.14
1380	13.8	197.7	842	1950	2792	0.13
1400	14.0	198.4	845	1947	2792	0.13
1420	14.2	199.0	848	1945	2793	0.13
1440	14.4	199.6	851	1942	2793	0.13
1460	14.6	200.2	854	1940	2794	0.13
1480	14.8	200.8	856	1938	2794	0.13
1500	15.0	201.5	859	1935	2794	0.12
1520	15.2	202.0	862	1933	2795	0.12
1540	15.4	202.6	864	1931	2795	0.12
1560	15.6	203.2	867	1928	2795	0.12
1580	15.8	203.8	870	1925	2795	0.12
1600	16.0	204.4	872	1923	2795	0.12
1620	16.2	204.9	875	1921	2796	0.12
1640	16.4	205.5	878	1919	2797	0.11
1660	16.6	206.1	880	1917	2797	0.11

| gauge pressure | | temperature in °C | Specific enthalpy | | | Specific volume steam |
in kPa	in Bar		water (h_f) (Sensible heat) in kJ/kg	evaporation (h_{f_g}) (Latent heat) in kJ/kg	steam (h_g) (Total heat) in kJ/kg	m^3/kg
1680	16.8	206.6	883	1914	2797	0.11
1700	17.0	207.1	885	1912	2797	0.11
1720	17.2	207.8	888	1910	2798	0.11
1740	17.4	208.3	890	1908	2798	0.11
1760	17.6	208.8	892	1906	2798	0.11
1780	17.8	209.4	895	1903	2798	0.11
1800	18.0	209.9	897	1901	2798	0.11
1820	18.2	210.4	900	1899	2799	0.10
1840	18.4	211.0	902	1897	2799	0.10
1860	18.6	211.5	904	1895	2799	0.10
1880	18.8	212.0	907	1893	2800	0.10
1900	19.0	212.5	909	1891	2800	0.10
1920	19.2	213.0	911	1889	2800	0.10
1940	19.4	213.5	914	1886	2800	0.10
1960	19.6	214.0	916	1884	2800	0.10
1980	19.8	214.5	918	1882	2800	0.10
2000	20.0	215.0	920	1880	2800	0.09

Index